P. Fletel.

16/-

PRINTING SCIENCE

PRINTING SCIENCE

By

F. PATEMAN

B.A., F.I.O.P.

Department of Printing, Watford College of Technology

and

L. C. YOUNG

B.Sc., A.R.I.C., F.I.O.P.

Department of Printing, Watford College of Technology

LONDON
SIR ISAAC PITMAN & SONS LTD.

First published 1963
Reprinted 1966

SIR ISAAC PITMAN & SONS Ltd.
PITMAN HOUSE, PARKER STREET, KINGSWAY, LONDON, W.C.2
THE PITMAN PRESS, BATH
PITMAN HOUSE, BOUVERIE STREET, CARLTON, MELBOURNE
22-25 BECKETT'S BUILDINGS, PRESIDENT STREET, JOHANNESBURG

ASSOCIATED COMPANIES
PITMAN MEDICAL PUBLISHING COMPANY Ltd.
46 CHARLOTTE STREET, LONDON, W.1
PITMAN PUBLISHING CORPORATION
20 EAST 46TH STREET, NEW YORK, N.Y. 10017
SIR ISAAC PITMAN & SONS (CANADA) Ltd.
(INCORPORATING THE COMMERCIAL TEXT BOOK COMPANY)
PITMAN HOUSE, 381-383 CHURCH STREET, TORONTO

MADE IN GREAT BRITAIN AT THE PITMAN PRESS, BATH
F6—(T.940)

PREFACE

THE increasing scientific content of training courses for craft students in the printing industry has led to an insistent demand for a book which would bring into a single volume an outline of the basic scientific principles of printing and their application. This book, based on our experience of teaching craft students at Watford College of Technology, is an attempt to meet that demand. Any such attempt must be highly selective in its approach both to the basic science and to the applications, leaving a large number of gaps to be filled by further reading. We have indicated at the end of each chapter, therefore, a few other books which could help the student to fill in more completely the background of knowledge demanded by a changing industry. These references, we hope, will also be of use to teachers, be they craftsmen or scientists, who are trying to teach the new syllabuses of the City and Guilds of London Institute examinations in printing subjects.

In the main we have covered all but the most highly specialized sections of these syllabuses up to the level of the final craft examinations, and the book will also serve as an introduction to the Full Technological Certificate course in applied science for those students and craftsmen who are seeking to widen their knowledge of the industry's problems.

Our thanks are due to Dr. W. Bleazard, Messrs. P. E. Watkins, A. H. Dawes, K. H. Mosedale, T. Pearman, and V. H. Rees for their advice and help with sections of the book, and to Mr. T. J. Cowley, the Head of the Department of Printing and Mr. L. S. Powell of Garnett College for their encouragement.

We also acknowledge gratefully the permission of the City and Guilds of London Institute for the reproduction of questions from their recent examinations, and the supply of or permission to reproduce diagrams by the Printing, Packaging and Allied Trades Research Association, British Drug Houses Ltd., Evans Electroselenium Ltd., Fry's Metal Foundries Ltd., the Monotype Corporation and Tintometer Ltd.

Finally, we must thank the printing students of Watford who checked many of the experiments outlined in the text and whose work with us will have been the basis for any success this book may have. For its failings we alone will bear the blame.

F. PATEMAN
L. C. YOUNG

Watford College of Technology
August, 1961

CONTENTS

LIST OF PLATES

(Between pp. 172 *and* 173*)*

LIST OF ABBREVIATIONS

c.c.	cubic centimetre
cm	centimetre
ft	foot
ft lb wt.	foot pound weight
gm	gramme
g.s.m.	grammes per square metre
in.	inch
kg	kilogramme
l.	litre
lb	pound
m	metre
mg	milligramme
ml	millilitre
mm	millimetre
μ	micron
mμ	millimicron
R.H.	relative humidity
V	volt
W	watt

Examples taken from recent City and Guilds of London examination papers are indicated by the year and grade—Intermediate and Final. In addition, the subject of the examination is indicated by key letters as follows—

205	Letterpress Machine Printing	.	.	.	Lp Mc
208	Monotype Casters' Work		.	.	Mono
209	Electrotyping and Stereotyping		.	.	E and S
210	Photoengraving				
211	Photogravure	.	.	.	Photo
212	Photolithography				
215	Lithographic Printing	.	.	.	Litho
217	General Bookbinding	.	.	.	BB
218	Publishers' Edition Binding	.	.	.	PEB
219	Printing Warehouse Practice	.	.	.	Wh
224	Applications of Science in Printing	.	.	FTC

CHAPTER I

SCIENCE AND PRINTING

PRINTING is an industry with a past. Although we can look back with pride on its achievements and cherish its traditions, we must avoid thinking that the methods and materials which have "stood the test of time" must necessarily be the best. It is this smug outlook which has labelled our industry as conservative and resistant to change.

Today, every industry is challenged to greater efficiency. Traditional methods and materials are no longer adequate to meet the demands of a highly competitive world. The printing industry is already finding new ways of doing old jobs: photocomposition, powderless etching techniques, the application of electronics in press controls and in platemaking. It is also making use of the properties of new materials like plastics, aluminium alloys, and diazo compounds. The pattern for the future is surely one of more change, as the advances in applied science in the past twenty years are exploited in our own industry.

As the printing industry changes, so do the demands made on its workers. The formation of the Institute of Printing in 1961 is symbolic of the industry's desire to advance its technology and to provide a nucleus of properly trained printing technologists. These backroom boys will always be the small minority. Skilled craftsmen will continue to form the backbone of the industry, but craft training alone will not provide them with the ability to adapt themselves to new techniques. A knowledge of the scientific principles which underlie printing processes is needed to meet the challenge of a changing industry.

The test of the craftsman comes when things go wrong. Too often it is a case of "try this," "try that," and the greatly overrated rule of thumb, instead of making a planned approach to a problem. This systematic approach is called *the scientific method*, but it would be quite wrong to think that this is some magic formula that scientists use to get all the right answers. Actually it is a method we all use at times but unfortunately not often enough. Successful research is only possible by its continuous application and this is one good reason why research work is not as glamorous as most people think. In order to make a systematic approach to a problem arising in a particular process, we must first know the factors influencing that process. For example, in trying to discover the reason why a poster has faded, we must know the factors which normally cause fading.

Put very briefly the scientific method of tackling problems goes like this—

(*a*) *Observe* all the facts.

(*b*) *Deduce* a hypothesis ("a guessed explanation of all the facts").

(*c*) *Test* the hypothesis by experiment and new observation.

(*d*) Either *improve* the hypothesis by stating it more accurately or *discard* it if the new observations show it to be false.

If experimental results support your hypothesis for a few hundred years then perhaps you would be justified in calling it a law! This explanation has only taken a few minutes, but the habit of using this method is not so easily acquired.

EXAMPLE

(*a*) **Observation of the Facts.** Every fourth sheet in a stack of printed labels is not drying satisfactorily.

Solid areas of ink on these particular sheets have a glossy appearance.

(*b*) **Deduction.** Since sheets following one another through the machine dry differently, the fault cannot be due to variations in the ink or in the atmospheric conditions. *Hypothesis*— Fault due to paper variation. The fact that every fourth sheet is different may be explained by the paper mill's method of slitting and sheeting reels.

(c) **Test of the Hypothesis.** Take an unprinted area from both a dry printed sheet A, and one on which drying is not satisfactory B. Compare these two papers for surface oil absorbency and for pH.

(d) **Observations**—

Paper A: surface oil absorption 85 sec, pH 6·2

Paper B: surface oil absorption 240 sec, pH 6·3

Hypothesis is supported. Every fourth sheet shows a low rate of oil absorption so that on this paper too much of this particular ink is remaining on the surface.

APPLIED SCIENCE IN THE PRINTING INDUSTRY

Although the amount of research in printing is small compared to many other industries, an important contribution is made by the research associations. In Britain, the Printing, Packaging and Allied Trades Research Association (PATRA) has grown steadily from the one-man inquiry bureau founded in 1930. Similar organizations exist in other countries and there is a good deal of international co-operation between them.

now also covers paper — known as PIRA

Considering the limited income available to PATRA, from members' subscriptions and a government grant made through the Department of Scientific and Industrial Research (DSIR), its field of activity is surprisingly large. Apart from doing basic printing and packaging research on problems ranging from second-impression set-off to the printability of ink and paper, PATRA provides an inquiry service dealing with day-to-day problems; a library and abstracting service; a critical-appraisals service; a machine testing service; a high-speed camera service; and an air-conditioning and factory-layout service. It is to be hoped that in the future the research associations will be used less for solving immediate problems so that more emphasis can be placed on long-term research into fundamentally new techniques like electrostatic printing.

A number of technologists are employed in the larger printing and packaging firms and laboratories exist for production control, research, and development. However, as is well known, our industry consists largely of very small units employing only a handful of people. Even a firm of moderate size employing several hundred may decide that equipping and staffing a control laboratory is beyond its resources. PATRA had these firms in mind when it introduced the test bench in 1960. It has been described as a "packaged laboratory" equipped with simple apparatus to enable the properties of paper and ink to be checked before printing and to assist in the investigation of everyday production problems. Used intelligently in conjunction with the PATRA inquiry service, it should greatly improve the efficiency of the smaller and medium-sized firms.

CHAPTER 2

METHODS OF MEASUREMENT

ACCURATE measurement is the lifeblood of science and technology. Aeroplanes, cars, watches, refrigerators, printing presses and all the other instruments and machines of our modern world are built up from parts which must be the right size. Precision methods have come more easily to new industries like electronics where they are starting from scratch, but in the older craft industries like printing the problem is greater, since old "rule of thumb" methods have had to be unlearnt and new methods put in their place.

A measurement must have two parts—a number and a unit. Thus we write 14 miles, 3·3 metres, 12 ounces, 7·2 grammes, 11·2 seconds and so on. We call the units of *length, mass* (what we normally call weight) and *time* the *fundamental units*, since many other units can be built up from these three, e.g. speed can be measured in miles per hour and density can be measured in pounds per cubic foot.

Unfortunately, in most countries units have developed in a haphazard fashion. A craft industry often devised its own system of measures and many of these have been retained. For instance in Britain, apart from the inches, feet, yards, and miles in general use, we still use the hand for measuring the height of a horse, the furlong for measuring race-tracks, the nautical mile for distances at sea, the fathom for the depth of the ocean, and many other strange units (Fig. 2.1). In printing, we use points and ems, a point being about $\frac{1}{72}$ in. and an em $\frac{1}{6}$ in.

With so many different units in existence and international trade increasing, there are very strong arguments for a simplified system of units which would be used by all nations.

1. **The Metric System.** The nearest approach to a universal system of units is the metric system, which was introduced immediately after the French Revolution. This

5

is used by scientists all over the world and in most countries other than Britain and America it is used for trade and commerce.

The system is based on the *standard metre* which is the distance between two fine lines marked on a platinum–iridium metal bar kept in the vaults of the International Bureau of Weights and Measures near Paris. A metre is just under 40 in., so a

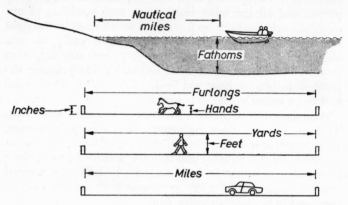

FIG. 2.1. SOME UNITS OF MEASUREMENT IN BRITAIN

sprinter who normally runs a hundred yards in England has to run about an extra nine yards if he is competing on the Continent or in the Olympic Games in the 100 metres.

The standard unit of weight on the metric system is the *kilogramme* which is the weight of a block of platinum–iridium kept in the International Bureau of Weights and Measures. The kilogramme is just under $2\frac{1}{4}$ lb.

The great advantage of the metric system is that it is a decimal system. The metric units larger than the standard are 10, 100, 1,000 . . . times the standard and the units smaller are $\frac{1}{10}$, $\frac{1}{100}$, $\frac{1}{1000}$ of the standard. Table 1 shows how these units of length and weight are derived from the standard metre and kilogramme. The names written in bold type are those most commonly used.

Table 1
THE METRIC SYSTEM

Length	Weight
1 **Kilometre** (km) = 1,000 m [approx. = $\frac{5}{8}$ mile]	1 **Kilogramme** (kg) = 1,000 gm [approx. = $2\frac{1}{4}$ lb]
1 Hectometre = 100 m	1 Hectogramme = 100 gm
1 Dekametre = 10 m	1 Dekagramme = 10 gm
1 **Metre** (m) [approx. = 39 in.]	1 **Gramme** (gm) [approx. = $\frac{1}{28}$ oz]
1 decimetre = $\frac{1}{10}$ m	1 decigramme = $\frac{1}{10}$ gm
1 **centimetre** (cm) = $\frac{1}{100}$ m	1 centigramme = $\frac{1}{100}$ gm
1 **millimetre** (mm) = $\frac{1}{1,000}$ m	1 **milligramme** (mg) = $\frac{1}{1,000}$ gm
1 micron (μ) = $\frac{1}{1,000,000}$ m	
1 millimicron (mμ) = $\frac{1}{1,000,000,000}$ m	

Notice that the Latin prefixes—

Kilo meaning 1,000

Hecto   ,,   100

Deka   ,,   10

deci   ,, $\frac{1}{10}$

centi   ,, $\frac{1}{100}$

milli   ,, $\frac{1}{1000}$

are used for units of both length and weight.

The advantages of the metric system are obvious when you

consider the equivalent English system of weights and their abbreviations.

$$
\begin{aligned}
16 \text{ ounces (oz)} &= 1 \text{ pound (lb)} \\
14 \text{ lb} &= 1 \text{ stone} \\
8 \text{ stone} &= 1 \text{ hundredweight (cwt)} \\
20 \text{ cwt} &= 1 \text{ ton}
\end{aligned}
$$

However, since the metric system and the English system are both used in industry, it is often necessary to convert a measurement from one system to the other. Two links between the two systems should be memorized; they are—

$$
\begin{aligned}
1 \text{ in.} &= 2 \cdot 54 \text{ cm} \\
1 \text{ lb} &= 454 \text{ gm}
\end{aligned}
$$

E.g. Convert 2 ft 3 in. to centimetres

$$2 \text{ ft } 3 \text{ in.} = 27 \text{ in.} = 27 \times 2 \cdot 54 \text{ cm} = 68 \cdot 58 \text{ cm}$$

Notice how easy it is to convert from one unit on the metric system to another.

E.g. Express 68·58 cm in: (a) millimetres; (b) metres

$$
\begin{aligned}
(a) \quad 68 \cdot 58 \text{ cm} &= 685 \cdot 8 \text{ mm} \\
(b) \quad 68 \cdot 58 \text{ cm} &= 0 \cdot 6858 \text{ m}
\end{aligned}
$$

It is done simply by moving the decimal point the appropriate number of places to the left or right. How many microns are there in one inch?*

Units of Area on the metric system are square centimetres (sq. cm) and square metres (sq. m)

E.g. Find the area: (a) in square centimetres; (b) in square metres, of a piece of paper 30 in. × 40 in.

$$
\begin{aligned}
\text{Area} = 30 \times 40 \text{ sq. in.} &= (30 \times 2 \cdot 54) \times (40 \times 2 \cdot 54) \text{ sq. cm} \\
&= 1{,}200 \times (2 \cdot 54)^2 = 7{,}741 \cdot 92 \text{ sq. cm} \\
1 \text{ metre} &= 100 \text{ cm}
\end{aligned}
$$

$$\therefore \qquad 1 \text{ sq. m} = 100 \times 100 \text{ sq. cm} = 10{,}000 \text{ sq. cm}$$

* There are 25,400 μ in one inch.

Area of paper—

$$\frac{7,741 \cdot 92}{10,000} = 0 \cdot 7742 \text{ sq. m}$$

Units of Volume on the metric system are—

cubic centimetres (c.c.) or millilitres (ml)
litres (l.)
cubic metres

1 litre = 1,000 c.c. or ml.

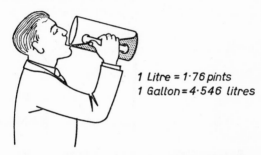

1 Litre = 1·76 pints
1 Gallon = 4·546 litres

FIG. 2.2. UNITS OF VOLUME—THE LIQUID MEASURE

The litre is used on the Continent as the liquid measure where we would use the pint or gallon. In France, instead of doing 30 miles to the gallon, your car would do about 10 kilometres to the litre. You might also be asked to "DRINKA LITRA MILKA DAY" (Fig. 2.2).

MEASURING DISTANCE

2. Degree of Error. In using a measuring instrument we are really estimating a quantity as accurately as the instrument will allow. Using an ordinary ruler we might decide that a certain distance was $5\frac{3}{10}$ cm or 5·3 cm. Yet the same distance measured with a more accurate instrument might prove to be 5·288 cm. Even that reading is only an approximation, and the completely exact measurement can never be made. It is important for us to know the limitations of a particular method of measuring and to take the possible error into account when using the result. In quoting a measurement, a scientist may indicate the possible *degree of error*, e.g.

$$5\cdot296 \text{ cm} \pm 0\cdot002 \text{ cm}$$

In other words the accuracy of the method of measuring is such that we can be certain the distance is not less than $5\cdot294$ cm and not more than $5\cdot298$ cm.

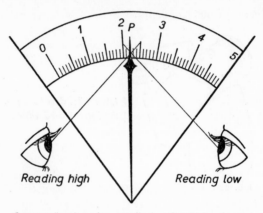

Correct reading along a line vertically above the point P on the paper

Fig. 2.3. Parallax Error

3. Parallax Error. You will have noticed that when you are reading a meter the position of your eye affects the scale reading. If you move your head to the left the reading is increased and if you move it to the right the reading is reduced. A correct measurement is taken when the eye is looking down the normal, i.e. the line at right angles to the scale and the pointer (Fig. 2.3).

This effect is called *parallax error*. It arises whenever the scale graduation of an instrument is not touching the point being measured. Measurements with a ruler are made more accurately if the ruler is turned on to its edge so that the scale is actually in contact with the point being measured.

4. The Vernier. If you examine a metre rule you will see that each small division represents $\frac{1}{10}$ centimetre or 1 millimetre. You will see also that these lines are about one-third as thick as the spaces between them. It would obviously be difficult to add more lines to increase the fineness of division and so with a ruler of this type you can only read to the nearest half millimetre. Exactly the same limitation applies to a ruler graduated in inches where the divisions cannot be smaller than $\frac{1}{64}$ in. and even then are difficult to read. Using a ruler with a vernier scale it is quite a simple matter to measure to the nearest $\frac{1}{100}$ cm ($\frac{1}{10}$ mm). A vernier consists of a second scale which slides alongside the main scale (Fig. 2.4 (a)).

The large divisions on the main scale are centimetres and these are divided into tenths (millimetres). Notice that the vernier scale is also divided into ten equal parts but these only cover $\frac{9}{10}$ cm on the main scale. In other words each small division on the vernier scale corresponds to $\frac{1}{10}$ of $\frac{9}{10}$ cm $= \frac{9}{100}$ cm. In Fig. 2.4 (a) since $BD = \frac{1}{10}$ cm and $BC = \frac{9}{100}$ cm then the very small distance

$CD = BD - BC = \frac{1}{10} - \frac{9}{100} = \frac{10}{100} - \frac{9}{100} = \frac{1}{100}$ cm

or 0·01 cm. The zero position on the vernier scale is exactly level with the 1 cm mark on the main scale and the distance $AB = 1\text{·}00$ cm (Fig. 2.4 (b)).

If we slightly increase the distance AB a point is soon reached where C marking the first division on the vernier scale is exactly level with D on the main scale.

Since $AD = 1\frac{1}{10}$ or $1\frac{10}{100}$ cm and $BC = \frac{9}{100}$ cm AB must equal $1\frac{10}{100} - \frac{9}{100} = 1\frac{1}{100}$ or 1·01 cm.

In just the same way if the second division on the vernier scale marked F comes level with the next mark on the main scale then AB measures $1\frac{2}{100}$ or 1·02 cm (Fig. 2.4 (c)).

As AB slowly increases this process of adding $\frac{1}{100}$ cm goes on until the vernier scale has moved $\frac{1}{10}$ cm and the original point B is level with point D on the main scale ($AB = 1\text{·}10$ cm).

Notice how we arrive at the reading 5·56 cm for the distance AB in Fig. 2.4 (d). 5·5 cm is the nearest graduation on the main scale *below* the distance being measured. The

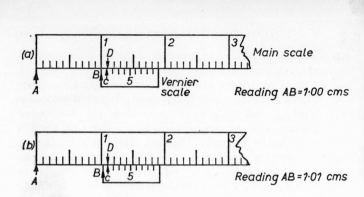

(a) Reading AB = 1.00 cms

Main scale
Vernier scale

(b) Reading AB = 1.01 cms

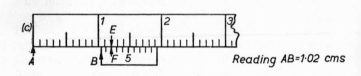

(c) Reading AB = 1.02 cms

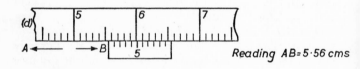

(d) Reading AB = 5.56 cms

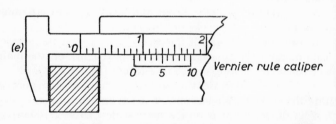

Vernier rule caliper

FIG. 2.4. THE VERNIER SCALE
(e) THE VERNIER RULE CALIPER

second decimal **6** is added to this because it is the **6th** division on the vernier scale which is exactly level with a graduation on the main scale.

A vernier rule caliper is shown in Fig. 2.4 (*e*). What is the length of the bar held in its jaws?*

Vernier scales are used on a large number of instruments where accurate measurement is important, e.g. microscopes, barometers, micrometers.

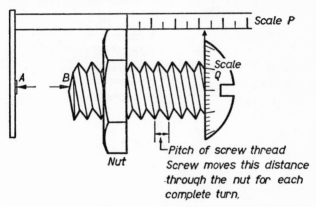

FIG. 2.5. THE MICROMETER

5. The Micrometer is the instrument commonly used for the accurate measurement of small distances, e.g. the size of type. English micrometers will measure to the nearest $\frac{1}{1000}$ in. or even less whilst those based on the metric system will measure to the nearest $\frac{1}{1000}$ cm.

Basically a micrometer is a calibrated screw. With each complete turn a screw moves through a nut, a distance equal to the pitch of the screw (Fig. 2.5). The scale *P*, fixed to the nut, is calibrated according to this pitch, and the fine movement of the screw is measured from the scale *Q* which runs round the screw head. Thus the distance *AB* can be read directly from the scales *P* and *Q*.

* The length is 0·85 cm.

In English micrometers the pitch of the screw is made $\frac{1}{40}$ in. (or 0·025 in.). The head of the screw is divided into 25 equal divisions and so each division will then represent $\frac{1}{25}$ of the pitch, i.e. $\frac{1}{1000}$ in. or 0·001 in.

The crude arrangement in Fig. 2.5 would not be reliable as a measuring instrument because the screw thread is exposed to dirt which would cause excessive wear on the nut. A simplified diagram of a modern micrometer screw gauge is shown in Fig. 2.6. The nut is fixed in a sleeve which forms an

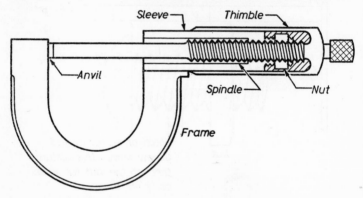

FIG. 2.6. A MICROMETER SCREW GAUGE

extension of the U-shaped frame. The spindle is threaded for about half its length so that the thread is protected from damage. The head of the screw is extended to fit over the sleeve like a thimble. A scale in $\frac{1}{40}$ in. corresponding to our P scale in the earlier diagram is engraved on the sleeve, and a scale in $\frac{1}{1000}$ in. corresponding to our Q scale is engraved on the thimble.

The object to be measured is placed between the jaws of the gauge and the screw turned until light contact is made. Most micrometers have a ratchet which ensures that the same pressure is applied every time. The reading is then taken, first from the sleeve scale and secondly from the thimble scale. Remember that on an English micrometer the sleeve scale is graduated in $\frac{1}{40}$ in. (0·025 in.) and the thimble scale in $\frac{1}{1000}$ in. (0·001 in.). Fig. 2.7 shows some typical readings and some others to work out for yourself.

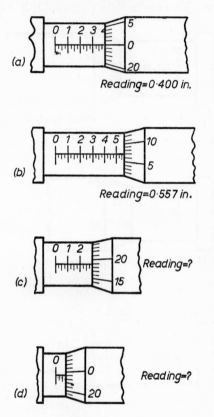

(a) *Reading=0·400 in.*

(b) *Reading=0·557 in.*

(c) *Reading=?*

(d) *Reading=?*

FIG. 2.7. TYPICAL READINGS ON AN ENGLISH MICROMETER

Metric micrometers have a screw with a pitch of $\frac{1}{2}$ mm so that in two complete turns it moves 1 mm. The sleeve scale is graduated in half-millimetres and the thimble scale has 50 divisions each representing $\frac{1}{100}$ mm (0·01 mm). Fig. 2.8

shows two typical readings of a metric micrometer and a third which is not worked out.

Before using a micrometer you should check that it reads zero when the jaws are in light contact. If it does not, then

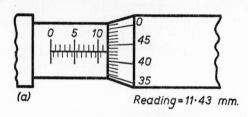

(a)   Reading = 11·43 mm.

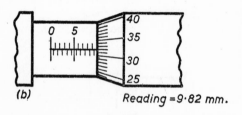

(b)   Reading = 9·82 mm.

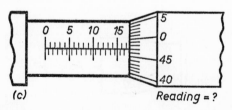

(c)   Reading = ?

FIG. 2.8. TYPICAL READINGS ON A METRIC MICROMETER

the reading should be noted and this *zero error* taken into account when making any measurement.

A micrometer screw gauge may be used to find the thickness of paper, but more often a paper micrometer is used which gives a direct dial reading of thickness under a standard pressure. This fixed pressure is necessary, since paper is a compressible material.

Direct dial readings can also be taken on gauges for measuring type height, depth of etch and roller setting.

6. Measuring Volume. The volume of a solid can often be found by making a direct measurement of its dimensions. We can only do this with liquids if we pour them into some

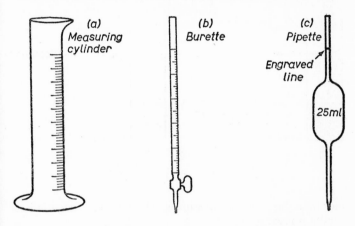

FIG. 2.9. MEASURING THE VOLUME OF LIQUIDS

regular-shaped vessel. The volume of liquid in a regular cylinder can be calculated by multiplying the depth of the liquid by the area of its circular cross section. When the cylinder is calibrated we call it a *measuring cylinder* or *graduated cylinder* (Fig. 2.9 (*a*)).

Measuring cylinders, made of glass or some transparent plastic, range in capacity from 5 c.c. to 2,000 c.c. You will have noticed how the surface of a liquid in a vessel is not completely flat. We call this curved surface the *meniscus*. The meniscus of most liquids, including water, curves upwards at the edges and in these cases readings should always be taken from the base of the curve (Fig. 2.10 (*a*)). On the

other hand mercury has a dome-shaped meniscus and readings
should be taken from the top of the curve (Fig. 2.10 (b)).
Although measuring cylinders are quick and easy to use they
do not provide an accurate method of measuring liquid
volume.

A *burette* is in effect a very tall, thin, measuring cylinder
fitted with a tap and fine opening at the lower end (Fig. 2.9 (b)).
This length and narrowness allows the graduations to be much

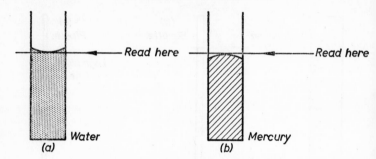

FIG. 2.10. HOW TO TAKE A READING

finer than they are on a measuring cylinder. The fine divisions
usually represent 0·1 ml.

The tap can be adjusted to vary the speed of delivery and
if necessary this can be reduced to a very slow drip.

A *pipette* is simply a narrow tube with a bulb in its stem
which tapers to a fine opening at its lower end (Fig. 2.9 (c)). It
is used to transfer an accurately measured fixed volume of
liquid from one vessel to another. The liquid is sucked up to a
level just above an engraved line on the stem. On taking the
pipette from the mouth, the liquid is held by a finger placed
tightly over the top of the stem. Then, by carefully relaxing
this pressure, the liquid level is allowed to fall to the engraved
line. Liquid should never be blown out of a pipette, but
allowed to flow out under gravity, leaving a small volume in
the jet which has been taken into account in its manufacture.
Pipettes with smaller capacities may have a graduated stem.

Burettes and pipettes play an important part in chemical analysis.

Methods of Weighing.   Most laboratory weighing is done on a chemical balance which is basically an accurately made pair of scales (Fig. 2.11).

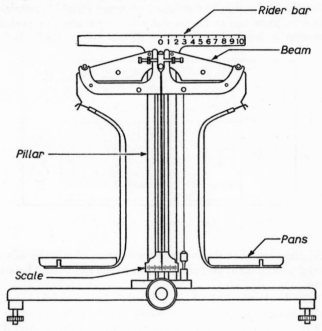

FIG. 2.11. A CHEMICAL BALANCE

The beam has a steel or agate* knife edge at its centre which rests on agate bearings.

The balance pans at either end of the beam are suspended on similar knife edges. Turning the knob clockwise raises the beam on to these knives and moving it back to its normal position relieves the knives, allowing the weight of the beam to fall on to the central pillar and the weight of the pans to

* *Agate* is an extremely hard natural form of silica.

rest on the base of the balance. Weights must only be added
or removed from the pan when the balance is in this rest
position or the knives and bearings will be damaged and
accuracy lost. A chemical balance should not be treated like a
pair of grocer's scales. Chemicals should not be placed
directly in the pan but weighed in some suitable container.
As a balance has to be carefully set up in any one position
moving it from place to place should be avoided. Before

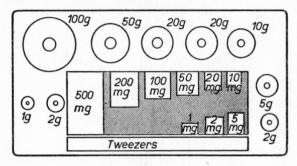

FIG. 2.12. THE LAYOUT OF A BOX OF WEIGHTS

weighing see that the balance reads zero, check the box of
weights (Fig. 2.12) and place it near to the right-hand balance
pan.

The knob should be turned slowly when a weight is being
tried since it is often unnecessarily time-wasting to move it
all the way to the right. In the early stages of weighing, it is
usually obvious as you begin to raise the beam that the weights
are either much too heavy or much too light. The weights
should always be returned to their correct positions in the
box. This saves a great deal of time in the long run. However tempting it may be, fingers should not replace the
tweezers. At the point of balance the weights on the pan should
be added and a note of the result made immediately. This
can then be checked by finding the total weight missing from
the box. Speed and accuracy develop with practice, provided
that weighing is approached methodically.

THINGS TO LEARN

1. On the metric system—

$$\text{Kilo} = 1,000$$

$$\text{centi} = \frac{1}{100}$$

$$\text{milli} = \frac{1}{1,000}$$

2. (a) On an English micrometer the pitch of the screw is $\frac{1}{40}$ in. and the head is divided into 25 equal divisions. Each

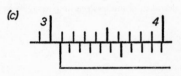

Fig. 2.13

division, therefore, records a movement of one thousandth of an inch.

(b) On a metric micrometer the pitch of the screw is $\frac{1}{2}$ mm and the head is divided into 50 equal divisions. Each division records a movement of one hundredth of a millimetre.

3. 1 in. = 2·54 cm approximately

1 lb = 454 gm approximately

OTHER BOOKS TO READ

L. S. POWELL, *Elementary Physics for Technical Students* (Pitman).

EXERCISES

1. Convert—

    (a) 381 cm to yards, feet, and inches.

    (b) 0·0356 m to centimetres.

    (c) 30 lb to kilogrammes and grammes.

2. Express the area of a piece of paper 22 in. × 30 in. in square metres (correct to 3 decimal places).

3. With the aid of diagrams explain the principle and purpose of a vernier scale. Make a sketch of a vernier scale reading 2·26 in.

4. Work out the measurements shown on the verniers in Fig. 2.13.

5. Describe an English micrometer screw gauge and how it may be read. Draw a micrometer scale reading 1·414 in.

6. Explain how you would measure accurately—

    (a) The height of a piece of type.

    (b) The weight of a sheet of paper.

    (c) 32·4 c.c. of water.

7. Draw vernier scales reading—

    (a) 0·37 in.

    (b) 2·89 in.

    (c) 1·21 cm.

8. Draw the scales of micrometers reading—

    (a) 1·822 in.

    (b) 0·691 in.

    (c) 1·218 cm.

CHAPTER 3

THE NATURE OF THINGS

If we cut a zinc plate into two and were able to go on dividing it into smaller and smaller parts we would eventually reach the smallest possible piece of the metal, an *atom* of zinc. Since there are about 270,000,000,000,000,000,000,000 atoms in one ounce of zinc, we would obviously not be able to make this division, nor would we be able to see a single atom under a microscope.

Elements. Zinc is one of the 92 natural *elements* which are the building bricks of our world, since all the materials we know, whether they be solids, liquids, or gases, are constructed from these elements. In addition, there are now ten man-made elements. We can define an element as a substance which cannot be split up into anything simpler by chemical means. As with zinc, the smallest whole unit of any one of these elements is an atom. We therefore have 102 different types of atoms, an atom of zinc being quite different from an atom of oxygen or an atom of uranium. Atoms of one element are all of the same type. Some of the more important elements are given in Table 2. You will recognize some of the important materials of the printing industry: lead, tin, and antimony, the constituents of type alloys; copper, zinc, aluminium, and magnesium used for printing plates; nickel and chromium used for facing printing surfaces; and silver which forms the black image on a photographic plate or film.

Symbols for the Elements. Notice that each element in the table is given a symbol which may be one or two letters. Where there is a second letter, it is always lower case, e.g. Na, Cu, Hg. These symbols give us a very useful form of "chemical shorthand," so that instead of writing "one atom of aluminium" we can simply write Al.

Compounds. Providing that it is pure, a zinc plate will consist only of zinc atoms. In practice, however, the atoms

Table 2
TABLE OF THE COMMON ELEMENTS

Atomic Number	Name	Symbol	Atomic Weight
13	Aluminium	Al	27·0
51	Antimony	Sb	121·8
56	Barium	Ba	137·4
35	Bromine	Br	79·9
48	Cadmium	Cd	112·4
20	Calcium	Ca	40·1
6	Carbon	C	12·0
58	Cerium	Ce	140·2
17	Chlorine	Cl	35·5
24	Chromium	Cr	52·0
27	Cobalt	Co	58·9
29	Copper	Cu	63·6
9	Fluorine	F	19·0
79	Gold	Au	197·3
2	Helium	He	4·0
1	Hydrogen	H	1·0
53	Iodine	I	126·9
26	Iron	Fe	55·9
82	Lead	Pb	207·2
3	Lithium	Li	6·9
12	Magnesium	Mg	24·3
25	Manganese	Mn	54·9
80	Mercury	Hg	200·6
42	Molybdenum	Mo	96·0
28	Nickel	Ni	58·7
7	Nitrogen	N	14·0
8	Oxygen	O	16·0
15	Phosphorus	P	31·0
78	Platinum	Pt	195·2
19	Potassium	K	39·1
14	Silicon	Si	28·3
34	Selenium	Se	79·2
47	Silver	Ag	107·9
11	Sodium	Na	23·0
16	Sulphur	S	32·1
50	Tin	Sn	118·7
92	Uranium	U	238·5
22	Titanium	Ti	48·1
74	Tungsten	W	184·0
30	Zinc	Zn	65·4

on the surface of the plate will readily combine with oxygen in the air to form a layer of zinc oxide, a white powder quite different from either the metal zinc or the gas oxygen. We call zinc oxide a *compound*. On the surface of the metal, atoms of the elements zinc and oxygen have chemically linked together (Fig. 3.1). We can define a compound as a substance consisting of two or more elements chemically linked together in definite proportions by weight.

In the case of zinc oxide, *one atom of zinc* has combined with *one atom of oxygen* and we can extend our chemical shorthand

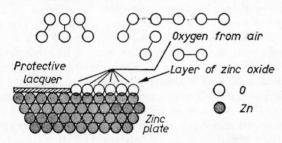

FIG. 3.1. THE FORMATION OF ZINC OXIDE

to write the *formula* of this compound as ZnO. In any sample of zinc oxide, the percentage by weight of zinc will be 80·25 and oxygen 19·75 since an atom of zinc is almost exactly four times heavier than an atom of oxygen. Different atoms do not always combine in this simple proportion of 1 : 1. For example, ammonia gas NH_3 consists of one atom of nitrogen combined with three atoms of hydrogen, and aluminium oxide Al_2O_3 consists of two atoms of aluminium combined with three atoms of oxygen. Potassium dichromate $K_2Cr_2O_7$ contains three different elements, potassium (two atoms), chromium (two atoms), and oxygen (seven atoms). Just as the twenty-six letters of the alphabet in different numbers and combinations can be built into tens of thousands of words, so the 102 elements in various arrangements make up over a million compounds. Some of these compounds like water, salt, polythene, and washing soda are familiar materials in our everyday lives. Others like nitric acid, "hypo," titanium dioxide, and toluene are vitally important chemicals in the printing industry.

Molecules. We have seen that the smallest whole unit of an element is an atom. In a similar way the smallest whole unit of a compound is called a *molecule*. A molecule of common salt, sodium chloride NaCl, consists of one atom of sodium combined with one atom of chlorine. One molecule of potassium dichromate consists of two atoms of potassium, two atoms of chromium and seven atoms of oxygen chemically linked together. In most cases elements exist as separate atoms, but there are a few important exceptions. The gases oxygen, hydrogen, nitrogen, and chlorine all link up into pairs of atoms as soon as they are formed in a reaction. A pair of hydrogen atoms H_2 is called a molecule of hydrogen.

Substances and Mixtures. So far we have only been considering pure substances which will be either elements or compounds. A piece of pure copper plate contains only copper atoms and if you chemically analyse any pure sample of sodium chloride you will always find that it contains 39·3 per cent sodium and 60·7 per cent of chlorine by weight. In other words *a substance is a material which has a constant fixed composition.*

A material in which two or more substances exist together without being chemically combined is called a mixture. The zinc plate with a layer of zinc oxide on its surface which we mentioned earlier is strictly a mixture. Sea water is a mixture of several salts including sodium chloride dissolved in water. Air is a mixture of nitrogen, oxygen, water vapour, carbon dioxide, and several other gases. Ink, paper, type metal, and petrol are all examples of mixtures of pure substances. Mixtures do not have definite compositions, since the substances contained in them may be mixed in almost any proportions. Unfortunately, it is often not possible to tell whether a material is a substance or a mixture simply by looking at it. Only chemical analysis will tell you accurately the composition of a material, but a few simple tests can give you some useful information.

EXPERIMENT. TO EXAMINE A NUMBER OF MATERIALS

1. *Appearance.* (a) Examine small quantities of a number of chemicals including crystals of sodium chloride, some iron filings and some powdered sulphur on a glass slide using a magnifying glass or a low powered microscope. Record your observations.

(b) Repeat using the given materials A and B (*see* Appendix). Record your observations and your conclusions.

2. *Solubility in Water.* (a) Shake a few grains of sodium chloride in about an inch of water (5 ml) in a small test tube. Repeat using iron filings and then sulphur and make a note of your observations.

(b) Repeat using the given materials A and B. Note your observations and conclusions.

3. *Action of heat.* (a) Heat a few grains of iron filings in an ignition tube and note the result. Repeat, using a small quantity of powdered sulphur.

(b) You have probably already decided that the mixture B is a mixture of iron and sulphur from its appearance and from the fact that in 2. they are separated, the iron filings sinking and the sulphur floating on the surface since its specific gravity is less than 1. They could also be separated with a magnet.

Now heat some of the material B in an ignition tube. Heating the two *elements* together starts a chemical reaction between them. When this reaction appears to be over, allow the tube to cool, break the base of the tube, separate some of the reaction product from the glass, and crush it to powder. Examine its appearance under a glass, its behaviour in water, and the effect on it of a magnet.

You will find that the material has no longer the properties of the original *mixture.* The two *elements* have combined together chemically to form the *compound*, iron sulphide, which has quite different properties from the two reacting elements.

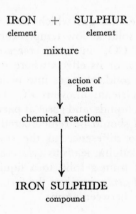

IRON + SULPHUR
element   element

mixture

action of
heat

chemical reaction

IRON SULPHIDE
compound

In any pure sample of iron sulphide the percentage by weight of iron is always 63·6 per cent and of sulphur 36·4 per cent. In other words, 6·36 gm of iron will react exactly with 3·64 gm of sulphur. If instead you took 8·36 gm of iron with 3·64 gm of sulphur, 2 gm of iron would take no part in the reaction and would remain at the end.

We can summarize what we have learnt about the various types of materials in the following table—

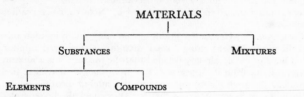

The Three States of Matter. If you heat a small piece of zinc plate in a nickel crucible over a bunsen burner it will soon reach the temperature (430°C) where the zinc becomes a liquid. If you go on heating, it can reach a temperature of 927°C when the liquid zinc changes into a vapour or gas. Soon after it escapes from the surface of the metal the zinc gas reacts with oxygen in the air to form "cobwebs" of white zinc oxide so we discover rather unexpectedly that zinc, which we normally think of as a very solid solid, can also be a liquid or a gas.

Carbon dioxide, the gas which we breathe out, can be converted into a solid at low temperatures. You may have come across "solid CO_2" in the ice cream trays brought round at cricket matches, or its effects where mist is required in a TV play. Ice, a solid, changes into a liquid (water) above 0°C and into a gas (steam) above 100°C. In fact, all substances can exist as solids, liquids, and gases at particular temperatures and pressures. It should be remembered that these changes of state make no difference to the substance chemically. Heating iron and sulphur leads to a *chemical change*, but heating zinc to change it from a solid to a liquid is only a *physical change*. A *chemical change* involves the forming or the breaking of chemical bonds between atoms.

In a solid substance like zinc the atoms are closely packed together. Often they fall into a regular pattern, when they appear as crystals. Though strongly held by its neighbours, each atom is in a constant state of vibration. The amount of vibration is increased as the substance is heated.

At a certain temperature (the melting point) all the atoms of a substance are moving so fast that the force of attraction between neighbours is not strong enough to prevent them

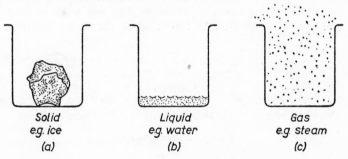

Solid
e.g. ice
(a)

Liquid
e.g. water
(b)

Gas
e.g. steam
(c)

FIG. 3.2. THE THREE STATES OF MATTER

moving about. This is the liquid state, where atoms no longer have to stay in fixed positions but are able to slide over their next door atoms to new neighbours. Whilst the atoms in a liquid have this increased freedom they still tend to cling together as a whole. This is demonstrated well by a drop of mercury on a plate or a drop of water on a greasy surface.

The speed of movement of the atoms in a liquid goes on increasing as the temperature is raised until a point is reached where all the atoms have sufficient energy to overcome the force of attraction that they have for one another. Rather like rockets being fired clear of the earth's gravitational pull, the atoms are now going fast enough to escape from the surface of the liquid. The atoms of a gas move freely in all directions and when enclosed they occupy all the available space (Fig. 3.2).

In this explanation of the three states of matter we have

talked about the motion of atoms in an element. Precisely the same reasoning applies for the movement of molecules in compounds, most of which can exist either as solids, liquids, or gases.

Water, the most common material we have, is familiar to us in these three states of matter. In ice, the molecules are held in a crystal structure, without the freedom to change places with one another. When the temperature of ice is raised above 0°C to become water, the molecules, moving faster, have gained this freedom, although they still tend to cling together as a whole. At 100°C when the water becomes

Proton
Unit positive charge
Mass =1 unit

Neutron
Neutral
Mass =1 unit

Electron
Unit negative charge
Mass =$\frac{1}{1,836}$ unit

FIG. 3.3. ATOMIC PARTICLES

steam, the molecules are moving sufficiently fast to escape and move into any available space.

The Structure of Atoms. We have seen that there are 102 different elements, and therefore 102 different types of atoms. Although these atoms are fantastically small, they are themselves built up from even smaller particles, *electrons*, *protons*, and *neutrons*. A copper atom differs from an oxygen atom or sulphur atom only in the numbers of each of these particles that it possesses and in the way in which they are arranged.

What are the differences between protons, electrons, and neutrons? The first point to remember is that whilst protons and neutrons have about the same mass, electrons only weigh a tiny fraction ($\frac{1}{1836}$) of that amount. Obviously then, electrons contribute almost nothing to the mass of an atom compared with the other two particles.

Atoms are small "solar systems" of electricity. Protons carry a unit positive charge, electrons carry a unit negative charge and neutrons, as the name suggests, are electrically neutral

(Fig. 3.3). Since atoms are themselves neutral, the number of electrons must always be the same as the number of protons.

We can picture an atom as having two parts—

1. *A heavy positive nucleus* or central core made up of protons and neutrons.

2. *Electrons* whirling round the nucleus and neutralizing its positive charge. (Fig. 3.4.)

The diameter of a hydrogen atom is about 100,000 times greater than that of the nucleus so the inside of an atom is

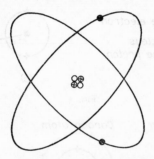

Fig. 3.4. An Atomic Model Showing Electrons Orbiting a Central Nucleus

mostly empty space. This may be clearer if you imagine that the nucleus was the size of a football, when the electron would be orbiting round it at distances up to ten miles in any direction.

An atom of any one element has its own particular number of electrons, protons, and neutrons. The lightest of all the elements, hydrogen, has an atom which simply consists of one electron orbiting a nucleus of one proton. We can best represent its structure in a diagram (Fig. 3.5 (*a*)).

The next simplest is another gas, helium (Fig. 3.5 (*b*)).

Following helium we have—

Lithium, 3 protons + 3 electrons.
Beryllium, 4 protons + 4 electrons.
Boron, 5 protons + 5 electrons.
Carbon, 6 protons + 6 electrons.

Nitrogen, 7 protons + 7 electrons.
Oxygen, 8 protons + 8 electrons.
Fluorine, 9 protons + 9 electrons.
Neon, 10 protons + 10 electrons.
Sodium, 11 protons + 11 electrons . . . and so on.

In addition to the protons and electrons, all these elements have neutrons in the nucleus, the numbers of which increase down the series but not in any regular fashion.

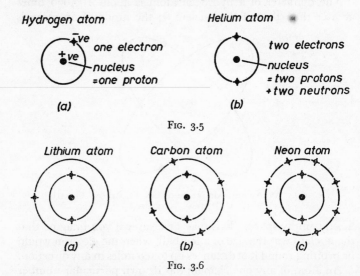

Hydrogen atom

one electron
nucleus
=one proton

(a)

Helium atom

two electrons
nucleus
= two protons
+ two neutrons

(b)

Fig. 3.5

Lithium atom   **Carbon atom**   **Neon atom**

(a)   *(b)*   *(c)*

Fig. 3.6

Notice that for a neutral atom the number of electrons always equals the number of protons. This number is called the *atomic number* of the element. The atomic number of oxygen = 8 and the elements range from hydrogen = 1 to the last of the natural elements, uranium = 92, and to the last of the ten man-made elements, nobelium = 102.

It is the arrangement of the electrons rather than the composition of the nucleus which tells us most about the way that an element behaves chemically. The paths of the electrons are arranged in shells rather like the layers of an onion.

Each shell will hold a certain number of electrons. For example, the shell nearest to the nucleus is complete with two electrons in it, so that the element lithium, which we saw has three electrons, has one of them in the second shell (Fig. 3.6 (a)) An atom of carbon with six electrons has four electrons in the second shell (Fig. 3.6 (b)). This shell will hold eight electrons so that the element neon has two complete shells of electrons (Fig. 3.6 (c)).

Sodium, the next element, with eleven electrons, has one of them in the third shell (Fig. 3.7 (a)). Chlorine with seventeen

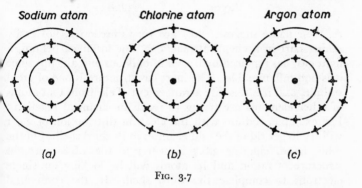

| Sodium atom | Chlorine atom | Argon atom |

| (a) | (b) | (c) |

Fig. 3.7

electrons has the distribution 2.8.7, and the electrons in an atom of argon are arranged 2.8.8 (Figs. 3.7 (b) and (c)). As the number of electrons increases towards the heavier elements, their arrangement becomes more complex.

Isotopes. There are actually three different types of hydrogen atoms. The second type, known as "heavy hydrogen" has one neutron in the nucleus in addition to the single proton and a third type known as "tritium" has two neutrons. Although these atoms have a different weight from a normal "light" hydrogen atom, their chemical properties are identical. Chlorine and magnesium are two other common elements with isotopes.

In all ordinary chemical reactions, such as the etching of a plate or the development of a photographic negative, it is only the electrons in the outside shell of an atom which change their positions. Whilst the amount of energy required to split off an outer electron from an atom is quite small, a great deal more is required to affect an electron nearer the nucleus, and still more to affect the nucleus itself.

Chemical Combination. The few elements which have all their electrons in completed shells are called the *inert gases*, e.g.

Helium	.	. 2
Neon .	.	. 2.8
Argon	.	. 2.8.8

As their name suggests, they are very unreactive, not easily taking part in a chemical reaction. For instance, helium, a light gas, has replaced hydrogen in balloons and airships since it is non-inflammable. The inert gas structure is one of great stability and it is this tidy arrangement of electrons that atoms of other elements are trying to reach in chemical reactions. For example, sodium with the electron distribution of 2.8.1 will try to get rid of the odd electron in its third shell. On the other hand, chlorine 2.8.7 is nearer to the 2.8.8 inert gas structure of argon and its atoms will be looking for single electrons to complete the third shell. In the compound sodium chloride NaCl an atom of sodium has given one electron to an atom of chlorine and both elements have reached a state of great stability. Substances which combine in this way by electron transfer are known as *electrovalent* (or ionic) compounds.

Notice that the atoms in this compound will carry an electrical charge. Sodium has only ten electrons to balance the eleven protons in its nucleus and it will therefore carry a unit positive charge. In a similar way chlorine will be negatively charged. These charged atoms are known as *ions*.

A crystal of sodium chloride actually consists of a lattice of the ions Na^+ and Cl^- (Fig. 3.9 (a)).

Silver bromide, the light-sensitive salt used in photography has a similar lattice structure (Fig. 3.9 (b)). There are other types of bonding between atoms in compounds. *Covalent*

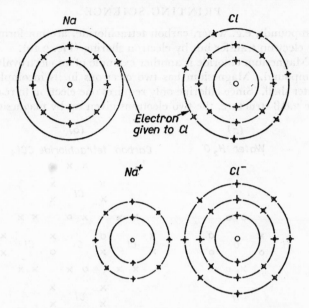

FIG. 3.8. AN ELECTROVALENT COMPOUND, SODIUM CHLORIDE

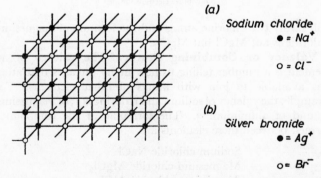

FIG. 3.9. CRYSTAL LATTICE

35

compounds, e.g. water, carbon tetrachloride, are not formed by electron transfer but by electron sharing (Fig. 3.10).

Magnesium chloride is another example of an electrovalent compound. Magnesium has two electrons in its incomplete outer shell. Since chlorine only requires one electron to reach the 2.8.8 structure, the two electrons given up by magnesium

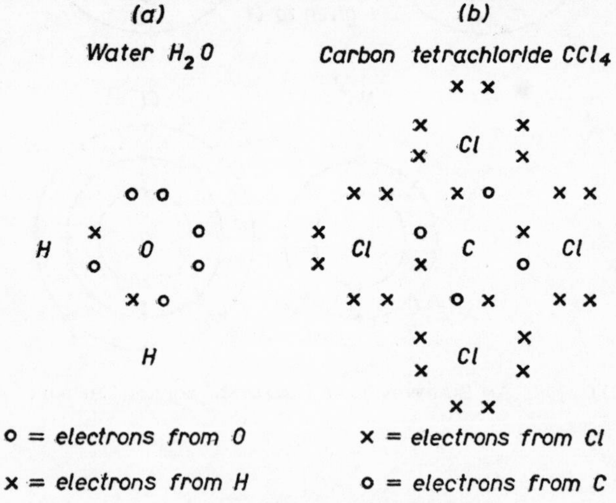

(a)

Water H_2O

(b)

Carbon tetrachloride CCl_4

o = electrons from O   x = electrons from Cl

x = electrons from H   o = electrons from C

FIG. 3.10. COVALENT COMPOUNDS
(Only outer electrons shown)

will satisfy two chlorine atoms and the formula of magnesium chloride is not MgCl but $MgCl_2$.

Valency or Combining Power. The valency of an element is a number telling us how many linkages that atom has available to join with atoms of other elements. For example, the valency of sodium and chlorine is 1, of magnesium 2, and of aluminium 3. The formulae of the compounds formed between these elements are—

Sodium chloride NaCl
Magnesium chloride $MgCl_2$
Aluminium chloride $AlCl_3$

A valency can also be given to a *radical* or group of atoms which tend to remain together in chemical reactions, e.g. —NO_3 the nitrate radical. It must be realized that a radical is only a part of a compound and does not have a separate existence. Some examples are given below of some important radicals with their sodium compounds.

—NO_3 the nitrate radical   Sodium nitrate $NaNO_3$
           valency = 1

—SO_4 the sulphate radical   Sodium sulphate Na_2SO_4
           valency = 2

—PO_4 the phosphate radical   Sodium phosphate Na_3PO_4
           valency = 3

The valencies of the important elements and radicals are nearly all between 1 and 4. In a number of cases, elements can show more than one valency. For example, iron (Fe) may be in a compound as ferric, valency = 3, as in ferric chloride $FeCl_3$, or as ferrous, valency = 2, as in ferrous chloride $FeCl_2$. Similarly copper may have a valency of 1 (cuprous) or 2 (cupric) and so there are two copper sulphates, cuprous sulphate Cu_2SO_4 and cupric sulphate $CuSO_4$—the familiar deep blue crystals.

Table 3 gives the valencies of all the common elements and radicals. If these can be memorized, it is quite a simple matter to build up the formulae of a very large number of compounds. In the cases of the elements with the variable valencies it is useful to remember that the form ending -ic is always a higher valency than that with the ending -ous, e.g.

Mercurous	1	Cuprous	1	Ferrous	2
Mercuric	2	Cupric	2	Ferric	3

You will probably gather from our brief look at how atoms combine that the valency of an element depends to a large extent on the number of electrons in the outer shell of its atoms. In fact these outer electrons are called *valency electrons*.

In forming electrovalent compounds the atoms or radicals either gain or lose electrons and therefore must either become

Table 3
SOME IMPORTANT VALENCIES

	Valency 1	Valency 2	Valency 3	Valency 4
Positively charged	Hydrogen H—	Magnesium Mg⟨	Aluminium Al⟨	Stannic Sn⟨⟨ (tin)
	Sodium Na—	Calcium Ca⟨	Ferric Fe⟨ (iron)	Carbon C= ⟨
	Potassium K—	Barium Ba⟨		
	Cuprous Cu— (copper)	Zinc Zn⟨		
	Silver Ag—	Mercuric Hg⟨ (mercury)		
	Mercurous Hg— (mercury)	Ferrous Fe⟨ (iron)		
	Ammonium NH₄—	Cupric Cu⟨ (copper)		
		Stannous Sn⟨ (tin)		

Negatively charged			
Chloride —Cl	Sulphide =S	Ferricyanide ≡Fe(CN)$_6$	Ferrocyanide ≣Fe(CN)
Bromide —Br	Oxide =O	Phosphate ≡PO$_4$	
Iodide —I	Sulphate =SO$_4$		
Cyanide —CN	Sulphite =SO$_3$		
Hydroxide —OH	Thiosulphate =S$_2$O$_3$		
Nitrate —NO$_3$	Carbonate =CO$_3$		
Acetate —CH$_3$COO	Chromate =CrO$_4$		
Permanganate —MnO$_4$	Dichromate =Cr$_2$O$_7$		

positively or negatively charged. In writing the formula of a compound one should always write the positively charged portion first. This will usually be a metal or hydrogen.

Examples of formulae derived from the valencies of the component parts—

1. Potassium nitrate	Potassium —nitrate	K —NO_3	valency = 1 valency = 1
	formula KNO_3		
2. Potassium dichromate	Potassium —dichromate	K —Cr_2O_7	valency = 1 valency = 2
	formula $K_2Cr_2O_7$		
3. Ferric sulphate	Ferric —sulphate	Fe —SO_4	valency = 3 valency = 2
	formula $Fe_2(SO_4)_3$		

Atomic Weights. Atoms of the various elements have different weights simply because they contain different numbers of protons and neutrons. Because atoms are so fantastically small, it is not convenient to use their *actual* weights. For instance, one atom of aluminium weighs about

$$\frac{1}{635,000,000,000,000,000,000,000,000}$$ of an ounce. As a piece of

information this is about as useful as knowing that there are about 11,658,000 inches between London and Manchester. It is more practical to use the relative weights of atoms, that is the weights of the atoms compared with the weight of one particular atom which is taken as a standard. If we take the weight of the lightest element, hydrogen, as being equal to 1, then the atomic weight of sodium whose atoms are about 23 times as heavy is equal to 23. Similarly lead, with atoms 207 times heavier than hydrogen atoms, has an atomic weight of 207. Formerly hydrogen was taken as the standard, but in recent times a very slight adjustment was made to all atomic weights, when for convenience the standard was changed to oxygen = 16, when hydrogen became 1·008. The atomic weights of the more important elements are shown in Table 2.

THINGS TO LEARN

1. Substances are materials with a constant fixed composition.

2. Substances may be either elements or compounds.

3. Any substance that we cannot divide by normal chemical methods and in which every atom is the same as every other atom is called an element.

4. Substances which consist of two or more elements chemically linked together in definite proportions are called compounds. A compound has properties which are quite different from those of the elements combined in it.

5. Any substance, depending on temperature and pressure, may exist as a solid, a liquid, or as a gas.

6. The atomic weight of an element is the weight of one atom of that element compared with the weight of one atom of oxygen, taking oxygen as 16.

OTHER BOOKS TO READ

P. S. JEWELL, *Elementary Principles of Chemistry* (University Tutorial Press)
F. W. GODDARD and K. HUTTON, *A School Chemistry for Today* (Longman)
W. M. SURTEES, *Elementary Chemistry for Technical Students* (Pitman)

EXERCISES

1. State the difference between: (a) an element; (b) a compound; and (c) a mixture. Give two typical examples of each.   (Photo/1960/Int.)

2. What do you understand by: (a) a physical change; (b) a chemical change? Give two examples of each.   (Lp Mc/1961/Int.)

3. What do you understand by the term valency? Given the valencies in Table 3 work out the chemical formulae of potassium bromide, zinc sulphate, calcium chloride, ammonium dichromate, ferric chloride, sodium carbonate, aluminium sulphate, potassium ferricyanide.

4. Define atomic weight. Given blocks of aluminium and silver of equal weight, work out the relative number of the two types of atoms in each (atomic weights, Al = 27, Ag = 108).

5. What are the names of the three basic particles which make up atoms? Show how these particles are arranged in an atom of oxygen.

6. Use the atomic structures of sodium and chlorine to show how the compound sodium chloride is formed.

CHAPTER 4

MATTERS OF WEIGHT

WHEN the first man lands on the moon, perhaps in a few years' time, he will find he is able to jump very much higher than he could on earth—much higher than the world high-jump champion. This is because his weight on the moon will be only a sixth of what it was on earth. Yet he will still have the same amount of flesh and bone on both planets. The amount of matter in an object is called its *mass* and so the mass remains the same wherever the object may be. The *weight*, however, is the force of gravitational attraction acting on it in a particular place. This force will be greater at sea level on earth than it will be on the top of a mountain or on the moon.

Weighing on a pair of scales or a chemical balance compares the mass of an object with the mass of the weights placed on the opposite pan (Fig. 4.1). As these masses remain the same everywhere, this method of weighing will give the same result for any object wherever it is carried out. A spring balance on the other hand measures the extension of the spring due to the gravitational force acting on the object attached to it. So a spring balance will record a lower weight for an object at the top of a mountain than it will for the same object at sea level—the difference is very small but it can be detected with a sensitive instrument.

For practical purposes the difference between mass and weight is often ignored, but the distinction is very important in some circumstances and should be remembered.

Density. If you hold a block of wood in one hand and a block of iron of the same size in the other the difference in their weights is very obvious. To make a proper comparison between the relative heaviness of one substance and another we must compare equal volumes, or more simply a unit volume of each.

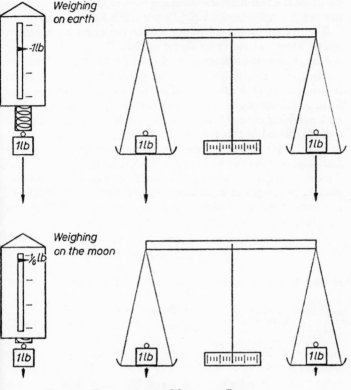

FIG. 4.1. DIFFERENCES IN WEIGHT AS RECORDED BY A
CHEMICAL BALANCE AND A SPRING BALANCE

The mass per unit volume of a substance is called its
density and may be expressed as—

$$\text{density} = \frac{\text{mass of object}}{\text{volume of object}} \qquad . \qquad . \quad (1)$$

The value obtained in this way will depend on the system of
units used. Water at a temperature of 4°C, for instance, has
a density of one gramme per cubic centimetre or 62·5 lb per

cubic foot, while the corresponding figures for iron are 7·5 gm per cubic centimetre and 465 lb per cubic foot.

The density of any substance will be the same (at any fixed temperature) whatever its shape or size. Because the volume will increase as the temperature rises while the mass will remain unchanged, density decreases as a substance gets hotter. Measurement of density will allow us to identify the material from which an object is made, as can be shown by measuring and weighing cubes of different materials and comparing the densities found in this way with a table of densities.

It is not very sensible, however, to use a figure which varies from one system of units to another. A more useful value than the density of a substance is its *specific gravity*. This is a comparison between the weight of a substance and the weight of the same volume of pure water at 4°C obtained from the equation—

$$\text{specific gravity} = \frac{\text{weight of substance}}{\text{weight of same volume of water}} \quad . \quad (2)$$

If we take unit volume in each case this becomes—

$$\text{specific gravity} = \frac{\text{density of substance}}{\text{density of water at } 4°C} \quad . \quad (3)$$

and so specific gravity is sometimes called *relative density*. Because it is the ratio between two quantities measured in the same units, specific gravity is just a figure which will remain the same for any substance whatever system of units we started with. By substituting in eqn. (3) the densities of iron and water given above in two different sets of units, we find the specific gravity of iron to be 7·5 in one case and 7·44 in the other. The slight difference arises because the densities given were approximate. Note that the specific gravity of a substance will change with temperature because its density at any temperature is being compared with the density of water at the fixed temperature of 4°C. Also, because the density of water in the metric system is 1 gm per c.c. the specific gravity of any substance is the same figure as its density on the metric system. The density of lead, for instance, is 11·34 gm per c.c. and its specific gravity 11·34.

To find the specific gravity of a liquid we use the types of specific gravity bottle shown in Fig. 4.2, the wide-necked

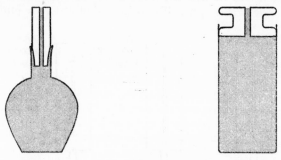

FIG. 4.2. TWO TYPES OF SPECIFIC GRAVITY BOTTLE

type being used for liquids such as oils, which are difficult to clean away.

EXPERIMENT. TO FIND THE SPECIFIC GRAVITY OF METHYLATED SPIRIT

Apparatus. Specific gravity bottle; chemical balance.

After making sure the bottle is thoroughly clean and dry, weigh it carefully and record the weight. Then fill it completely with distilled water and replace the stopper. Wipe excess water from the top of the stopper with non-absorbent material and dry the outside of the bottle completely before weighing. Empty the distilled water and wash the bottle and stopper in methylated spirit to remove all the water. Fill the bottle with methylated spirit, taking the same precautions as before, and reweigh. Subtract the weight of the bottle from the other two weights recorded and divide the weight of methylated spirit by the weight of water.

Suppose the results obtained in the above experiment were: empty bottle 20·3 gm; bottle and water 69·7 gm; bottle and liquid 60·4 gm. Then—

$$\text{weight of liquid is } 60·4 - 20·3 = 40·1 \text{ gm}$$

$$\text{weight of water is } 69·7 - 20·3 = 49·4 \text{ gm}$$

$$\text{So specific gravity} = \frac{\text{weight of liquid}}{\text{weight of water}} = \frac{40·1}{49·4} = 0·81$$

ARCHIMEDES' PRINCIPLE

When a piece of metal is hung from a spring balance the balance records its weight. If the metal is now immersed in a container of water the pointer of the balance will show a lower weight (Fig. 4.3). If now instead of water we immerse

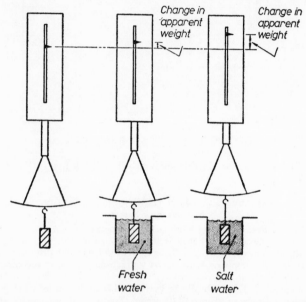

Fig. 4.3

the metal in a solution of salt, as strong a solution as we can make, the balance will record a still lower weight. The loss of weight is only apparent, because each time we remove the metal from the liquid the balance again records the original weight.

As the apparent loss in weight varies with the liquid in which we immerse the metal, there must be some connexion between the liquid and the apparent amount of weight lost. To find out what this connexion is we repeat the experiment above with a small beaker on the pan of the balance and with the liquids into which the metal is to be immersed held in graduated cylinders (Fig. 4.4). In each case the rise of liquid in the cylinder when the metal is immersed will be the same. It will, in fact, be equal to the volume of the piece of metal. In each case also the pointer of the balance can be brought

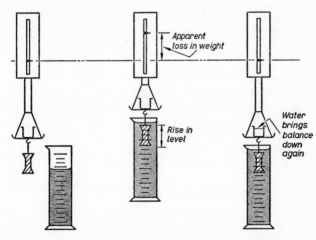

Apparent loss in weight

Rise in level

Water brings balance down again

FIG. 4.4

back to the original position by pouring into the beaker on the pan the same volume of liquid as the metal has displaced in the cylinder.

This demonstrates the truth of the principle, first stated by the Greek philosopher Archimedes, that—

When an object is wholly or partly immersed in a liquid the apparent loss in weight is equal to the weight of liquid displaced.

The same is true for any fluid, including a gas.

Apparent loss in weight arises from the fact that the liquid exerts an upthrust on the object equal to the weight of the displaced volume of liquid.

As the apparent loss in weight of a solid object is the weight of the liquid it displaces, we can find the weight of the volume of water equal to the volume of any solid body by weighing the body in air and then totally immersed in water and so finding the apparent loss in weight. From eqn. (3) above we see—

$$\text{specific gravity} = \frac{\text{weight of object}}{\text{apparent loss in weight}} \qquad . \quad (4)$$

For example, if we have an object which weighs 100 gm in air and apparently weighs 91 gm in distilled water then its specific gravity will be $\dfrac{100}{9} = 11 \cdot 1$.

Although this will be true for any solid body, it will not be true if the body is hollow, as is obvious from the fact that iron bars sink while iron ships float. In the case of a hollow body the value of the specific gravity obtained will be an average for the whole volume instead of just for the volume of the shell. This can be used to find the proportion of empty spaces (or voids) in a piece of type without cutting it open.

Experiment. To Find the Volume of Empty Space in a Piece of Type Metal

Apparatus. Type metal of known specific gravity; balance bridge; beaker with distilled water.

Hang the type metal from the arm of the balance and note its weight. Place the beaker of distilled water on the bridge over the pan of the balance in such a position that the metal can be weighed while totally immersed but not in contact with the side or bottom of the beaker. The apparent loss in weight in grammes will be the same figure as the total volume in cubic centimetres, because the weight of 1 c.c. of distilled water is 1 gm. Compare this with the volume calculated from the specific gravity of the metal. The difference between the two will be the volume of empty space.

Suppose the piece of metal used in the experiment above weighed 20·4 gm and its apparent loss in weight was 2·14 gm. Then the total volume of metal and spaces would be 2·14 c.c. If the specific gravity of the metal was 10·8 then the volume of metal would be $\dfrac{20 \cdot 4}{10 \cdot 8} = 1 \cdot 89$ c.c. The volume of empty space, therefore, must be given by $2 \cdot 14 - 1 \cdot 89 = 0 \cdot 25$ c.c.

Floating Objects. In cases where the average specific gravity is less than one, the object will float in water. As can be seen from Fig. 4.5, any floating object is subject to two forces—its weight W acting downward and the upthrust T of the displaced liquid. When these become equal the object can sink no deeper. Because the upthrust is equal to the weight of liquid displaced, if we make the water denser by dissolving salt in it the object will not sink as deeply as in water

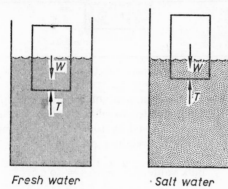

Fresh water   · Salt water

FIG. 4.5

alone. A ship therefore floats higher in the sea than it does in the fresh water of a river.

This principle is applied in practice to measure the specific gravity of liquids by means of an instrument called the *hydrometer*. The most common type of hydrometer consists of a glass tube weighted at the bottom so that it will float upright. The upper part, which is long and narrow, is marked either directly with the specific gravity of the liquid in which it sinks to that level, or in some arbitrary scale of numbers such as the Twaddell scale or Beaumé scale. These scales measure the specific gravity of liquids in terms of arbitrary "degrees." By varying the loading of the lower bulb, hydrometers can be made to cover small ranges of specific gravity, as is the case with hydrometers for measuring the strength of etching solutions or battery acid.

BULK VALUE

Printing inks present something of a problem in the measurement of specific gravity because they are neither solids nor simple liquids. It is not possible to use a hydrometer because the structure built up by particles of pigment and the liquid vehicle prevent the instrument from sinking to its proper depth. The density of the ink is found by weighing a specimen

FIG. 4.6. FINDING THE DENSITY OF INK

of the ink in a recess of known volume in a glass plate (Fig. 4.6). This is then converted to what is called the *bulk value*— that is, the volume occupied by 100 gm. For example, if the volume is 2 c.c. and the weight 4 gm then

$$\text{bulk value} = \frac{2 \times 100}{4} = 50 \text{ c.c.}$$

THINGS TO LEARN

1. Mass is the quantity of matter in an object.

2. Weight is the gravitational force acting on an object.

3. Density is the mass of an object divided by its volume.

4. Specific gravity is the mass of an object divided by the mass of the same volume of water.

5. Archimedes' Principle states that when an object is weighed in air and then partly or totally immersed in a liquid the apparent loss in weight is equal to the weight of liquid displaced.

OTHER BOOKS TO READ

L. S. POWELL, *Elementary Physics for Technical Students* (Pitman)
M. NELKON, *Principles of Physics* (Christophers)

EXERCISES

1. What do you understand by: (*a*) absolute density and (*b*) specific gravity (relative density)?   (Lp Mc/1960/Int.)

2. (a) Define density. (b) How would you find the density of a piece of zinc?   (E and S/1960/Int.)

3. Describe: (a) a laboratory method for accurately determining the specific gravity of a liquid, and (b) the use of a hydrometer for adjusting the relative density of a solution.   (Photo/1954/Int.)

4. What is the difference between density and specific gravity? The density of lead is 11·34 gm per c.c. and of aluminium 2·70 gm per c.c. Find the volume occupied by one kilogram of each.

5. Explain why any object with specific gravity less than 1 will float in water. If a wooden rod of the same area of cross-section throughout its length of 20 cm is floated upright in distilled water what length will sink below the surface when the density of the wood is 0·8 gm per c.c.?

6. What is meant by bulk value? Find the bulk value of an ink of density 1·25 gm per c.c.

7. Calculate the volume of empty space in a piece of metal weighing 25·8 gm in air and 23·16 gm in water if the specific gravity of the metal is 11·2.

8. Describe two methods of determining the density of a plating solution.
                                                             (E and S/1959/Fin.)

CHAPTER 5

HEAT AND HUMIDITY

FOR the printer the weather is important not only when he goes on holiday, but all the time he is working. Two aspects of the weather—temperature and humidity—have a considerable effect on paper, ink, and other materials. Temperature indicates the hotness or coldness of a body. Humidity indicates how much moisture is present in a material or in the atmosphere.

TEMPERATURE SCALES

Just as there are different systems for measuring length so there are different systems for measuring temperature. The *Fahrenheit* scale is in everyday use in this country, the *centigrade* or *Celsius* scale is in use in Europe and in scientific work, while the *absolute* or *Kelvin* scale is used for a large number of scientific purposes. From Fig. 5.1 you can see how the three are related to the fixed points of the temperature of boiling water and the temperature of melting ice at normal pressure.

The temperature $0°K$, which is the same as $-273°C$, is a very special one. It is the coldest that anything in the universe can be—at that temperature all movement of the molecules of a substance ceases. That is why it is chosen as zero on this scale.

As both absolute and centigrade scales have 100 divisions between the lower and upper fixed points, all we have to do to convert centigrade temperatures to absolute is to add 273 to allow for the difference in zero position. Thus $55°C$ is $(55 + 273)°K = 328°K$ and $475°K = (475 - 273)°C = 202°C$.

In converting from Fahrenheit to centigrade, however, we have to take into account that between the fixed points there are 100 divisions on the centigrade scale and 180 on the Fahrenheit. Therefore, 100 centigrade divisions are equal to 180 Fahrenheit divisions and so 5 centigrade divisions equal 9 Fahrenheit divisions.

To convert from one of these to the other we always start at the lower fixed point. For example, in converting 55°C to Fahrenheit—

55°C is 55 divisions above the lower fixed point.

$$55 \text{ centigrade divisions} = \frac{55 \times 9}{5} \text{ Fahrenheit divisions}$$

$$= 99 \text{ Fahrenheit divisions.}$$

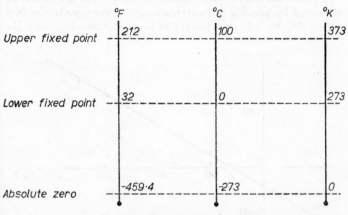

FIG. 5.1. TEMPERATURE SCALES

Thus there are 99 Fahrenheit divisions above the lower fixed point, which in this case is 32. Therefore

$$55°C = (99 + 32)°F = 131°F.$$

The same procedure is used for conversion in the other direction. For example, 126°F is (126 − 32) divisions above the lower fixed point, that is 94 divisions above. But

$$94 \text{ Fahrenheit divisions} = \frac{94 \times 5}{9} = 52 \cdot 2 \text{ centigrade divisions.}$$

As the lower fixed point on the centigrade scale is zero, 126°F = 52·2°C.

5—(T.940)

These calculations can be put in the form of standard equations for converting any temperature T on one scale to the other as follows—

$$T°C = \frac{9T}{5} + 32°F \qquad . \qquad . \qquad . \quad (1)$$

$$T°F = \frac{5(T - 32)}{9}°C \qquad . \qquad . \qquad . \quad (2)$$

To save the labour of calculation a conversion graph can be obtained by placing a Fahrenheit and a centigrade thermometer side by side in a beaker of ice water and warming the

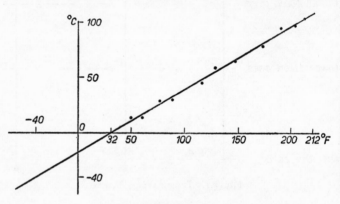

FIG. 5.2. PLOTTING A GRAPH FROM THE READINGS OF
TWO THERMOMETERS

water slowly with a low bunsen flame. The readings of the two thermometers are taken together and plotted on a graph, as in Fig. 5.2. It will be found that they lie on a straight line which cuts the Fahrenheit axis at 32° and passes through the point 100°C, 212°F. Any point on this line for a given centigrade temperature will show the corresponding Fahrenheit temperature and vice versa.

MEASURING TEMPERATURE

The most common way of measuring temperature is by using a thermometer, which is a closed glass tube holding mercury or alcohol, the latter being used for low temperatures at which mercury would freeze. As these expand more than glass when heated they will rise higher in the tube as the surrounding temperature rises. Examining a thermometer you will notice that the bulb at the bottom is made of very thin glass to allow the mercury in it to adjust itself as quickly as possible to the surrounding temperature. As mercury is a very good conductor of heat, most of the delay in adjustment will be due to

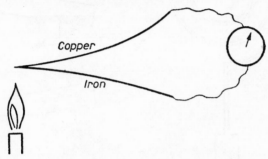

FIG. 5.3. THE THERMOCOUPLE

the glass. The tube in which the mercury or alcohol rises is made very narrow so that the top of the column moves a large distance for a small change in temperature.

It is not always convenient to use as fragile an instrument as a thermometer for measuring temperature on machines. A fairly common alternative is the *thermocouple* which consists of two wires of different materials joined together at one end and with their free ends connected to an instrument able to measure small electric currents. When the junction between the two wires is warmed the electric current set up will make the pointer of the instrument swing to one side (Fig. 5.3). The amount of swing depends on the difference in temperature between the junction and the free ends of the wires. It can be used therefore to measure the temperature around the junction. Many printing machines are fitted with this device.

Other methods of measuring temperature depend on the expansion of a metal strip (PATRA stack thermometer), change in electrical resistance of a platinum wire (platinum resistance thermometer), comparing the colour of a furnace with that of a heated wire (hot wire pyrometer), etc.

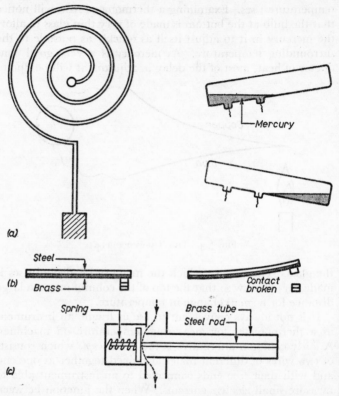

Mercury

(a)

Steel

(b)

Brass

Contact broken

Spring

Brass tube

Steel rod

(c)

FIG. 5.4. THREE TYPES OF THERMOSTAT

Thermostats. For many purposes we need not only to measure the temperature but also to maintain it at some fairly steady level. This is necessary on typecasting machines, on some gluing machines, or when burning in some acid resists. Instruments used to control temperature are called *thermostats*.

Some thermostats use the expansion of metals with rising

temperature to operate a switch or valve. One of these is the bourdon tube used on Monotype casters. A metal tube full of mercury ends in a spiral with a lever attachment. As the mercury expands the tube unwinds slightly under the pressure set up, causing the lever to tip a mercury switch (Fig. 5.4 (a)) and so switching off the current for the electric heater. By the reverse process the current is switched on again as required to maintain the correct temperature.

The most common type of expansion thermostat is a strip of two metals, such as steel and brass, welded or riveted together. Because brass expands more than steel for a given rise in temperature the strip bends and switches off heater current when the desired temperature is reached (Fig. 5.4 (b)). By attaching a pointer moving over a graduated scale to the strip, it can be used as a thermometer. A valve made of steel and brass used for controlling gas or steam heaters is shown in Fig. 5.4 (c). The valve closes as the expansion of the brass tube moves the end of the steel rod to the right.

Some other types of thermostat are electrical, a thermo-couple or the change in the resistance of a platinum wire being made to give an electric current which moves a switch or valve to change the amount of heat supplied.

Melting and Boiling. The melting or boiling points of pure substances are quite clearly defined and we can give an exact temperature at which the transition from one state to the other will take place. There is a clear "arrest point" in the rise or fall of temperature as a substance changes state.

EXPERIMENT 1. TO FIND THE MELTING POINT OF LEAD

Apparatus. Fine lead shavings; crucible; Bunsen or mekker burner; high temperature thermometer.

Place the shavings in the crucible with the thermometer tube showing above an asbestos lid. Heat the crucible slowly until the metal is completely molten taking the thermometer reading at one minute intervals. Plot the temperature readings against the time at which they were taken. Remove the burner and again plot the readings until all the metal is solid again.

The form of graph obtained by the experiment above is shown in Fig. 5.5, the flat part of the curve showing the melting point of lead as 327°C or 621°F. If we were to do the same thing with shavings of a mixture of lead, tin, and antimony—a type metal—we should get a graph like that in

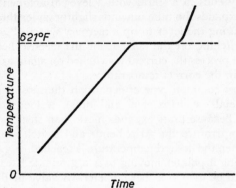

FIG. 5.5. GRAPH SHOWING THE MELTING POINT OF LEAD

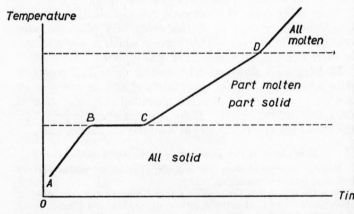

FIG. 5.6. GRAPH SHOWING THE MELTING RANGE OF AN ALLOY

Fig. 5.6. In the region *B* to *D* some of the mixture is solid and some liquid. The mixture has a *melting range* instead of a fixed melting point, and this range will vary according to the proportions of the metals used (*see* Chapter 14).

A similar situation arises at boiling point. The pure forms of the solvents xylene and toluene have fixed boiling points but the commercial mixtures known as xylol and toluol used in gravure inks boil over a range of temperatures (*see* Chapter 20).

MEASURING HEAT

Using the same-sized Bunsen flame on each occasion, it will be found that it takes much longer to raise the temperature of 100 gm of water by the same number of degrees than it does for 100 gm of copper. As the flame will be giving out heat at the same rate on each occasion this time difference must be due to water needing a greater quantity of heat to bring about the change than copper requires. For each substance there is a fixed amount of heat, called the *specific heat* of the substance, which is needed to raise the temperature of unit weight of the substance by one degree.

On the metric system the unit used for measuring the amount of heat is the *calorie*, which is the amount needed to raise the temperature of one gramme of water by one degree centigrade. A larger unit is the great or kilogram Calorie which is 1,000 calories. In Britain we often use the British Thermal Unit (Btu) which is the amount of heat required to raise the temperature of one pound of water by one degree Fahrenheit. The specific heat of a substance is thus the number of calories needed to raise the temperature of one gramme of the substance by one degree centigrade or the number of British Thermal Units to raise the temperature of one pound of the substance by one degree Fahrenheit.

Different substances will also absorb different amounts of heat when they melt or boil. The number of calories needed to melt or boil one gramme of the substance without changing its temperature is called its *latent heat* of fusion and evaporation respectively. On the British system, latent heat is expressed in British Thermal Units.

EXPERIMENT 2. TO FIND THE SPECIFIC HEAT OF COPPER

Apparatus. Pieces of copper; copper calorimeter; large can lined with cotton wool; accurate thermometer; balance.

Sufficient small pieces of copper to bring the total weight to about 250 gm are placed in the calorimeter and then carefully weighed. The calorimeter is placed in the nest of cotton wool in the larger can as shown in Fig. 5.7. Take the exact temperature of some water heated to about 50°C and pour this into the calorimeter until it is half full. Stir well and

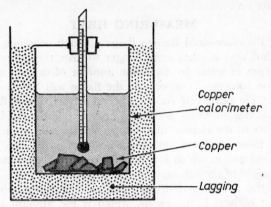

FIG. 5.7. FINDING THE SPECIFIC HEAT OF COPPER

measure the temperature when the thermometer shows a steady reading. Find the weight of water added by re-weighing the calorimeter.

Suppose the readings made in the above experiment were—

Weight of calorimeter and copper . . 246·4 gm
Weight of water added . . . . 134·1 gm
Rise in temperature of calorimeter and copper 30°C
Fall in temperature of water . . . 5°C

Then the gain in heat by the calorimeter and copper is given by $246·4 \times 30 \times c$ where c represents the specific heat of copper.

The loss of heat by the water will be $134·1 \times 5$ calories, and if we assume no heat loss to the surrounding air these two quantities will be equal. Therefore—

$$246·4 \times 30 \times c = 134·1 \times 5$$

so $$c = \frac{134·1 \times 5}{246·4 \times 30} = 0·090 \text{ calories per gramme.}$$

Because our assumption that no heat at all is lost to surrounding air is not quite true, the value for the specific heat obtained in this way is usually a little below the correct figure of 0·093 calories per gramme.

A very similar experiment can be carried out to find the latent heat of fusion of ice.

EXPERIMENT 3. TO FIND THE LATENT HEAT OF FUSION OF ICE

Apparatus. Lumps of ice; filter paper; copper calorimeter and jacket; thermometer; balance.

Weigh the empty calorimeter and then weigh it again after it has been half filled with warm water. Place the calorimeter in a cotton wool nest as in the previous experiment and record the temperature of the water. Quickly dry a few pieces of ice with filter paper and drop them into the calorimeter stirring well until the thermometer shows a steady reading. Now re-weigh the calorimeter to find how much ice has been added.

Typical results of such an experiment might be as follows: weight of calorimeter 84·94 gm; weight of warm water 102·12 gm; weight of ice 21·82 gm; temperature before adding ice 30°C; final temperature 12°C.

We can now calculate the losses in heat as loss by calorimeter $84·94 \times 0·093 \times 18 = 142·19$ cal; loss by water $102·12 \times 18 = 1,838·16$ cal; giving a total heat loss of 1,980·36 cal.

Against this must be set the gain in heat of the ice first of all in melting and then in rising from 0°C to 12°C.

Heat gained in melting is $21·82 \times L$ cal where L is latent heat of fusion of ice; heat gained during temperature rise—

$$21·82 \times 12 = 261·84 \text{ cal,}$$

so total gain is $261·84 + 21·82 L$ cal.

As the loss will be equal to the gain—

$$21·82L = 1,980·36 - 261·84 = 1,718·52 \text{ cal}$$

from which we get $L = 79$ calories per gramme (the actual value is 80 calories per gramme).

The latent heat of substances is nearly always larger than the specific heat, so more heat is required to melt metal or to evaporate a solvent than is needed just to raise the temperature.

Much more heat is needed, for instance, to melt completely a pot of stereo metal than to raise the temperature to melting point. That is one reason why the metal in large platecasting machines is kept in a molten state instead of being allowed to solidify overnight.

RELATIVE HUMIDITY

Any container of water left standing without a cover will gradually evaporate away even though the water never approaches boiling point. This is because the molecules in their constant movement are continually colliding with each other and changing speed so that a few are able to reach the speed at which they can escape from the liquid. As the most common liquid in the world is water there is always a certain amount of water vapour in the atmosphere. The amount of water vapour present in any volume of air can be measured and is called the *humidity* of the air. For most purposes, however, and for all printing processes, we are interested in what is called *relative humidity* rather than in humidity as such.

At any given temperature there is a limit to the amount of water vapour a given volume of air can hold. When this limit is reached a balance is struck between the number of molecules of water escaping into the atmosphere and the number condensing out of it in the form of dew. The amount of moisture necessary to saturate a given volume of air increases as the temperature rises. Warm air will hold more water vapour than cold air—as can be seen when the windows of a bus or train mist over with a film of moisture deposited on them when the warm air inside is cooled by the glass. Cooling of the air in the evening or during the night causes dew to fall and this evaporates away again as the air gets warmer after sunrise.

In the same way, a stack of cold paper unwrapped in a warm warehouse or machine room will cool the air in its immediate neighbourhood and lead to the edges of the sheets becoming damp and distorted. To avoid this the temperature of the paper should be measured by pushing the flat tube of a PATRA stack thermometer through the outer wrapping before the paper is exposed to the atmosphere of the printing works.

The paper should not be unwrapped until its temperature rises to that of the factory.

The transfer of moisture between paper or other substances and the atmosphere depends on relative humidity, that is, on how near the air is to saturation.

Relative humidity is expressed numerically as the amount of water vapour actually present divided by the amount necessary to saturate the same volume at the same temperature. The fraction so obtained is multiplied by 100 to bring it to a percentage. Thus—

$$RH = \frac{\text{amount of water vapour present}}{\text{amount of water needed for saturation}} \times 100 \text{ per cent}$$

The air in a room at 75 per cent relative humidity has three-quarters of the water vapour needed to saturate it at the temperature then prevailing. If the temperature now falls without any change in the amount of water vapour present the relative humidity will increase because the fall in temperature has reduced the amount of water vapour needed to saturate the air. The opposite happens when the temperature rises. So in order to control the relative humidity of a room we must control both the temperature and the amount of water vapour.

Measuring Relative Humidity. Measuring relative humidity (often abbreviated to r.h.) by extracting the water vapour from a sample of air and weighing it, would be much too difficult an operation for everyday use. We therefore make use of secondary effects.

At sometime or another most of us have found which way the wind is blowing by wetting a finger to find which side became colder when exposed to the wind. This cooling is due to the water evaporating into the air playing on the finger. The water takes the latent heat necessary for its evaporation from the underlying flesh and blood. We feel much cooler as a summer breeze dries sweat from our bodies. The faster the rate of evaporation the greater the cooling effect.

The *wet and dry bulb hygrometer* makes use of this effect to measure relative humidity. It consists of two thermometers, one fully exposed to the air and the other wrapped in a piece of cotton fabric kept wet by trailing in a small container of water. The wet bulb is cooled by water evaporating from the fabric.

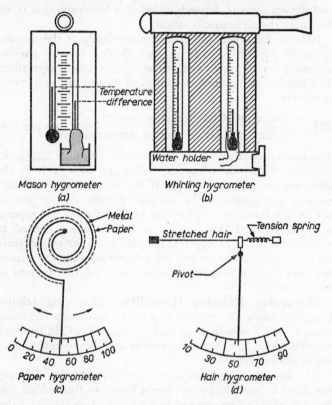

Temperature difference

Water holder

Mason hygrometer
(a)

Whirling hygrometer
(b)

Metal
Paper

Stretched hair

Tension spring

Pivot

0 20 40 60 80 100

Paper hygrometer
(c)

10 30 50 70 90

Hair hygrometer
(d)

Fig. 5.8. Four Types of Hygrometer

The lower the relative humidity, the faster evaporation will take place and the greater will be the difference between the temperatures shown on the two thermometers. To find the relative humidity the reading of the dry bulb and the difference in temperature between it and the wet bulb are compared with humidity tables prepared by the Meteorological Office. These set out the relative humidities for all combinations of these two readings.

Wet and dry bulb hygrometers are found in the forms shown in Fig. 5.8 (a) and (b). The former is fixed to a wall and should be fanned while the readings are being taken to avoid a purely local build-up of water vapour around the wet bulb with a consequent reduction in the rate of evaporation. The latter can be carried round the room and rotated like a football fan's rattle, so maintaining a regular flow of air over the wet fabric. An average of readings taken in different parts of the room will provide the best indication of relative humidity.

Another type of hygrometer uses the expansion of paper as a means of measuring relative humidity. The paper pasted on the outside of a coiled metal spring will expand with increasing relative humidity making the spring coil more tightly and the pointer to move to the right across the scale (Fig. 5.8 (c)). A fall in relative humidity will cause the pointer to move in the opposite direction. Human and animal hair also changes length as relative humidity changes. This fact is the basis of the hair hygrometer of which the principle is shown in Fig. 5.8 (d). The hair is sometimes stretched down a long perforated tube which can be inserted into a pile of paper or other material to measure the relative humidity of the air in contact with the paper. It is then known as a sword hygrometer. Both the paper and hair hygrometers have to be calibrated by comparison with the wet and dry bulb type. Details of the effect of relative humidity on materials will be found in the appropriate chapters later in this book.

Air Conditioning. The relative humidity of a factory is kept at a fixed level as part of the process known as air conditioning. An apparatus on the roof of the building draws in air which it cleans, warms or cools to the right temperature, and either dampens or dries to the desired relative humidity. The conditioned air is fed through the factory in sufficient quantity to ensure that no untreated air gets in to upset the balance achieved. When only a limited area needs to be conditioned temperature can be held steady by thermostats and extra moisture added to the air as required. This is a compromise system which will not be really effective when external temperature or humidity rise above the desired level.

THINGS TO LEARN

1. The two fixed points of temperature are the boiling point of water and melting point of ice at normal pressure.

2. The lower fixed point is 0° on centigrade and 32° on the Fahrenheit scale. The upper fixed point is 100°C and 212°F. Five centigrade divisions equal nine Fahrenheit divisions.

3. One calorie is the amount of heat required to raise the temperature of one gramme of water by one degree centigrade.

4. Specific heat is the amount of heat required to raise the temperature of one gramme of a substance by one degree centigrade.

5. Latent heat is the amount of heat required to melt or evaporate one gramme of a substance without changing its temperature.

6. Relative humidity is the ratio of water vapour actually present to the amount required to saturate the same volume of air at the same temperature—given as percentage.

7. To control relative humidity it is necessary to control both temperature and the amount of water vapour present.

OTHER BOOKS TO READ

L. S. POWELL, *Elementary Physics for Technical Students* (Pitman)
LITHOGRAPHIC TECHNICAL FOUNDATION, *Paper and Humidity in the Pressroom* (L.T.F. New York)

EXERCISES

1. Water boils at 212°F/100°C and freezes at 32°F/0°C. Show how this information can be used in the conversion of temperatures on the Fahrenheit scale to temperatures on the centigrade scale.   (Photo/1961/Int.)

2. It is necessary to cast at 710°F but your regulator is marked in centigrade only. At what point must the regulator be set?

(Mono/1959/Int.)

3. What is the function of a thermostat? Outline briefly the operation of two different types of thermostat.

4. Explain why there is a temporary check in the increase in temperature of a heated pot of metal when the metal begins to melt. How much heat would be needed just to melt 150 gm of lead shavings if the shavings were at 20°C? The melting point for lead is 327°C, its specific heat 0·032 calories per gramme per °C and latent heat 6 calories per gramme.

5. Distinguish between the following: (a) heat and temperature; (b) density and specific gravity; (c) specific heat and latent heat of fusion.

(E and S/1959/Int.)

6. (a) Describe briefly the principles underlying two instruments for measuring the temperature of molten metal.

(b) You are melting a slug casting metal and you believe your instrument may be incorrect. How would you check this, no pyrometer being available? (E and S/1960/Fin.)

7. What do you understand by the term relative humidity? How is it determined? (Lp Mc/1959/Int.)

8. (a) Explain the meaning of relative humidity. (b) Show how it can be measured with wet and dry bulb thermometers. (Photo/1959/Fin.)

9. (a) What is the effect of changes in humidity in the letterpress machine room? (b) Describe briefly how you could measure such changes.

(Lp Mc/1961/Int.)

10. (a) Define relative humidity. Why may temperature changes alter relative humidity? (b) Air conditioning involves the control of three main factors. What are they? Outline the means usually employed to control each factor. (BB/1960/Fin.)

CHAPTER 6

HOW MACHINES WORK

WHEN we push a small object along a table with the index finger it will move in the direction the finger is pointing. By changing the direction of the push we change the direction of movement. When both index fingers are used, pointing in different directions, the object will move along a line which lies in between the directions in which the fingers are pushing. In each case the fingers exert a force on the object, and it is important to notice that a force has direction as well as size. When two forces act on one object at the same time we cannot add them together in the same way as we add numbers but must also take into account their direction.

ADDING FORCES

A convenient way of adding forces together can be demonstrated by the following experiment, the layout of which is illustrated in Fig. 6.1.

EXPERIMENT 1. TO FIND THE SIZE OF A FORCE BALANCING
TWO OTHER FORCES ACTING ON THE SAME POINT

Apparatus. Wooden frame with pegs; three spring balances; string.

Three pieces of string, each attached to a spring balance, are firmly tied together at a point O as in Fig. 6.1. With the strings lying just above and parallel to the surface of a large sheet of paper in the frame fix the balances to pegs in the frame. Draw lines on the paper to coincide with each string and mark on them distances OA, OB, and OC in proportion to the force exerted by the balance attached to that string. Complete the parallelogram $OADB$. It will be found that the diagonal OD is the same length as and in line with the line OC. Repeat for different directions of the strings and different forces on the balances.

Any two forces can in fact be combined by drawing lines which represent them in both size and direction and then completing what is known as the *parallelogram of forces*. The diagonal of the parallelogram so formed represents their resultant in both magnitude and direction. As the experiment above shows, when three forces are in balance the resultant

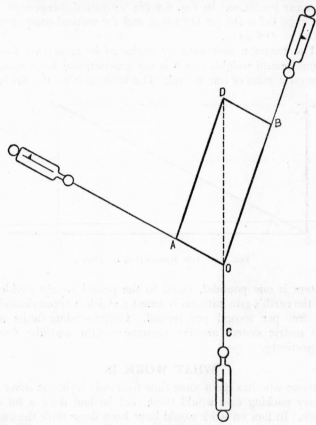

FIG. 6.1. ADDING FORCES

of any two of these forces must be equal in size and opposite in direction to the third.

Because any two forces have a single resultant, we can equally represent a single force by two forces acting in appropriate directions, usually along two lines at right angles to each other. This process of representing one force by two others is known as *resolution* of forces and is used for convenience in many problems. In Fig. 6.2 the horizontal component of the force *OA* is *OB* (or *OA* cos *a*) and the vertical component is *OC* (or *OA* sin *a*).

The common unit used by engineers in measuring force is one pound weight, which is the gravitational force which acts on a mass of one pound. The basic unit on the British

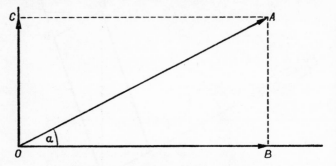

FIG. 6.2. THE RESOLUTION OF FORCES

system is one poundal, equal to the pound weight divided by the earth's gravitational constant g which is approximately 32 feet per second per second. Corresponding units on the metric system are the gramme weight and the dyne respectively.

WHAT WORK IS

Anyone who has spent some time fruitlessly trying to move a heavy packing case would think that he had done a lot of work. In fact no work would have been done until the case had changed its position. *Work* is defined as the size of the force multiplied by the distance the force moves in the direction of operation. In equation form

$$\text{work} = \text{force} \times \text{distance} \qquad . \qquad . \qquad (1)$$

When the force is measured in pounds weight and the distance in feet, then the unit of work done is one foot pound weight (often wrongly abbreviated to foot pound). Suppose we have a sack of waste metal weighing 112 lb lifted to the tailboard of a lorry 3 ft 6 in. from the ground. The work done will be 112 lb wt. × 3·5 ft, that is, 392 ft lb wt. This will be the result whether we give a straight lift as in Fig. 6.3 (a) or lift and carry before putting it on the lorry as in Fig. 6.3 (b). In the second case the extra distance BC is at right angles to

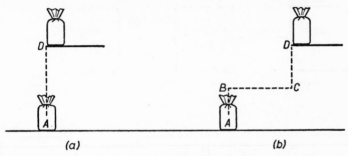

(a)   (b)

FIG. 6.3. MEASUREMENT OF WORK

the lifting force F, not in the direction of its operation. This distance makes no contribution to the work done.

The *energy* of a body is its capacity to do work and might be regarded as stored work. When we lifted the sack to the lorry's tailboard we increased its energy by 392 ft lb wt. by changing its position—this form of energy is called *potential energy* or energy of position. If we let the sack fall off the tailboard the potential energy is changed into energy of movement, which we call *kinetic energy*. Whenever we use a mallet or hammer we lift it to give it potential energy, then allow it to fall to transform the potential into kinetic energy which then does useful work such as driving a nail, planing a forme, etc.

When kinetic energy is used in this way not all of it is changed into useful work—some of it is lost as heat, which is another form of energy. Energy is constantly being changed from one form to another but it is never destroyed. The law of *conservation of energy* is one of the most important laws governing the way things happen in the universe. The chain of events by which we get the energy to move our printing machines is as follows: light energy from the sun was stored as chemical energy in plants growing thousands of years ago; these plants became coal which we dug up to use as fuel; burning the coal changes the chemical energy into heat; the heat produces steam which gives kinetic energy to the moving parts of a dynamo; this kinetic energy becomes electrical

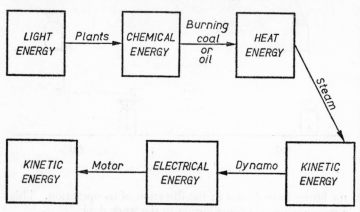

Fig. 6.4. Forms of Energy

energy which is carried along wires to a motor; the motor converts electrical energy into kinetic energy of the moving parts of our machine. The whole chain is shown in Fig. 6.4.

Describing the capacity of a motor to do work we usually use the word *power* rather than energy. Power is the rate at which work is done or energy converted. Thus

$$\text{power} = \frac{\text{work done}}{\text{time taken}} \qquad . \qquad . \qquad . \qquad (2)$$

In the British system of units power is measured in foot pounds weight per second, the practical unit being horsepower, which is a rate of 550 ft lb wt. per sec. So a motor of five horse-power can do work at the rate of $550 \times 5 = 2{,}750$ ft lb wt. per sec.

Turning Effect. So far we have discussed the way forces behave along their own line of action, the way we push open a sliding door. But most doors open by turning about a pivot or hinge, and it is common experience that the further from the hinge we push the door the easier it is to open it. This is because the turning effect of a force depends not only on its size but also on its perpendicular distance from the pivot. The turning effect of a force about a point is called the *moment* of the force about that point. In Fig. 6.5 the line *AB* represents

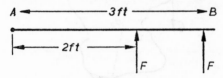

FIG. 6.5. MOMENT OF A FORCE

a door hinged at *A*. If we push the door 3 ft from the hinge with a force of 4 lb wt. then the moment about *A* is 4 lb wt. × 3 ft = 12 lb wt. ft, but if we use the same force 2 ft from the hinge the moment will be 4 × 2 = 8 lb wt. ft.

When a number of forces are acting on the same object some will be trying to turn it in a clockwise direction and some anti-clockwise as in Fig. 6.6. The resulting moment about the point *O* in a clockwise direction will be $F_1 d_1 + F_2 d_2 - F_3 d_3$. The object will be in equilibrium when the resulting moment is zero.

All these ideas of force, work, power, and so on are used in the design of machines whatever they may produce. Some machines seem very complicated, but they are complicated only because they are made up of a large number of parts each quite simple in itself. There are only a small number of these simple machines.

Levers. The simplest and oldest of all machines is the lever, used to overcome a large resistance at one place by a small effort exerted at another. An example of the first class of lever is the crowbar (Fig. 6.7 (*a*)) which pivots about the point *O*, known as the fulcrum. The load *W* will then move when the moment of the effort E about O becomes greater than the moment of the load about O. Suppose W is 120 lb wt. and the distances OA and OB are 5 in. and 45 in., the

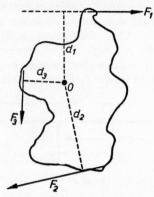

FIG. 6.6. FORCES ACTING UPON AN OBJECT

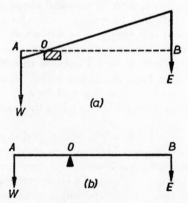

FIG. 6.7. THE FIRST CLASS OF LEVER

system will be in equilibrium when the moments about O are equal, that is, when 120×5 equals $E \times 45$. So the load will be moved by any force greater than 13·3 lb wt. if we ignore the effect of friction.

The *mechanical advantage* of any machine is defined as the ratio $\dfrac{\text{load overcome}}{\text{effort applied}}$.

In the case of the crowbar this is 120 lb wt. divided by 13·3 lb wt., that is 9, the same as the ratio between the two

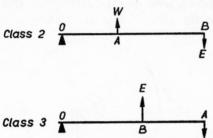

FIG. 6.8. THE SECOND AND THIRD CLASSES OF LEVER

distances. Looking at Fig. 6.7 (*b*) we see that this is always so for this class of lever, for

$$W \times OA = E \times OB$$

and so

$$\text{mechanical advantage} = \frac{W}{E} = \frac{OB}{OA} \qquad . \quad (3)$$

The feature of the first class of lever is that the load and the effort are on opposite sides of the fulcrum, so a bodkin used to raise a line of type in a tight forme is also a class one lever, as is a Linotype key, a platen treadle and many other parts you can see on various machines.

The second and third classes of lever are shown in Fig. 6.8. Notice that both are pivoted at one end. In the class two lever the effort is always further from the fulcrum than the load, while in class three the effort is always nearer the fulcrum than the load. In each case, taking moments about the fulcrum O, we get the equation

$$W \times OA = E \times OB \qquad . \qquad . \qquad . \quad (4)$$

which is the same as for the class one lever. Thus we see that
for any class of lever the mechanical advantage is equal to the
perpendicular distance of the effort from the fulcrum divided
by the perpendicular distance of the load from the fulcrum.
Examples of the class two lever found in printing are the hand
guillotine and the lever slug and rule cutter. Class three is to
be found in the take-off of a Wharfedale and the second

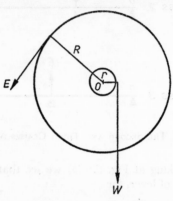

FIG. 6.9. DIAGRAMMATIC REPRESENTATION OF THE WHEEL
AND AXLE MACHINE

elevator arm of a Linotype—other examples you can find in
plenty.

Wheel and Axle. Another very common type of simple
machine is the wheel and axle, shown in diagrammatic form
in Fig. 6.9. If the radius of the wheel is R and the radius of the
axle r, the system will be in equilibrium when moments about
O are equal, that is when $W \times r = E \times R$. So, neglecting
the effect of friction, we have—

$$\text{mechanical advantage} = \frac{W}{E} = \frac{R}{r} \quad . \quad . \quad (5)$$

Looking at Fig. 6.7 and Fig. 6.9 it can be seen that any
mechanical advantage gained is offset by the fact that the
effort has to be moved much further than the load moves.

For every simple machine there is a value known as the *velocity ratio* given by—

$$\text{velocity ratio} = \frac{\text{distance moved by effort}}{\text{distance moved by load}} \quad . \quad (6)$$

In the case of the wheel and axle, for each turn of the wheel the load will be raised by a distance equal to the circumference of the axle, i.e. $2\pi r$. At the same time the effort will move through a distance equal to the circumference of the wheel, i.e. $2\pi R$. Therefore

$$\text{velocity ratio} = \frac{2\pi R}{2\pi r} = \frac{R}{r} \quad . \quad . \quad (7)$$

It is important to notice that the mechanical advantage in real machines is always below the theoretical value because part of the effort is used to overcome friction and the weight of moving parts. The velocity ratio is not affected, however, because it depends only on the dimensions of the machine. For this reason we must have some way of describing the *efficiency* of a machine, that is, how much of the work put into it can be applied to useful purposes. This is defined by—

$$\text{efficiency} = \frac{\text{work got out}}{\text{work put in}} \quad . \quad . \quad (8)$$

The work obtained from the machine will be the load $\times$ distance moved by load. The work put in will be the effort $\times$ distance moved by effort. Thus—

$$\text{efficiency} = \frac{\text{load} \times \text{distance moved by load}}{\text{effort} \times \text{distance moved by effort}} \quad . \quad (9)$$

Comparing this with the definitions of mechanical advantage and velocity ratio, we see—

$$\text{efficiency} = \frac{\text{mechanical advantage}}{\text{velocity ratio}} \quad . \quad . \quad (10)$$

Experiment 2. To Find the Mechanical Advantage, Velocity Ratio and Efficiency of a Wheel and Axle

Apparatus. Wheel and axle; slotted weights and hangers.

Hang a known weight from the axle and hang other weights from the rim of the wheel until the load on the axle just begins to move. Then measure the distance moved by the weights on the rim for a given distance moved by the load. From the figures obtained work out the three values. Repeat for different loads and then see the effect of increasing friction by pressing a felt pad on the axle.

Suppose in the above experiment a weight of 0·5 lb just moved a load of 4 lb. Then the mechanical advantage would

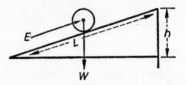

FIG. 6.10. THE INCLINED PLANE

be 8. If the load lifted 2 in. for a movement of the effort of 20 in. the velocity ratio would be 10, and from eqn. 10 the efficiency would be 0·8 or 80 per cent. As the friction increases the efficiency will be found to decrease.

Inclined Plane. The inclined plane, often found in the form of a wedge, is also very familiar to printers. It is used in locking up type and for moving reels of paper into position. In Fig. 6.10 the reel being moved up the step, which is h ft high, weighs W lb wt. The ramp being used is L ft long and the effort being applied is E lb wt. The work done in raising this reel will be $W \times h$, and the work done by the effort will be $E \times L$. Ignoring friction these will be equal, therefore—

$$W \times h = E \times L$$

and mechanical advantage $= \dfrac{W}{E} = \dfrac{L}{h}$ . . (11)

To take a practical example, a 500-lb reel can be raised 2 ft using an 8 ft ramp by a push of only 125 lb wt.

Screw. In the very early days of printing all machines worked on the basis of the screw, which gives a big pressure when a relatively small force is applied. We still use the same principle in the familiar book press and it also has many other applications. A screw may be regarded as an inclined plane wrapped round a central support. In the press shown in Fig. 6.11 the screw has four threads to the inch and thus

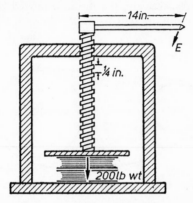

FIG. 6.11. A SCREW BOOK PRESS

the platen will move down $\frac{1}{4}$ in. in one turn. If the work in the press offers a resistance of 200 lb wt. to compression, then the work done in one turn of the screw will be 200 × 0·25 = 50 in. lb wt. In one turn the effort E has moved right round the circle described by the handle. If this handle is 14 in. long the work put into the press will be $E \times 2 \times \frac{22}{7} \times 14$ = 88 E. If we ignore the effect of friction these will be equal, and hence $E = \frac{50}{88} = 0·57$ lb wt. So you will see that the mechanical advantage offered by a screw system is very large, but so is the velocity ratio; therefore such machines are slow in operation, as you may have discovered in practice.

Machine Drives. Printing machines, like all other machines, may be driven from the motor by a belt, a chain or by gear wheels meshing directly together. The relative sizes of the wheels are chosen to suit the speeds of the motor and the machine it is driving. In Fig. 6.12 we have a driving pulley of diameter d on a motor running at r revolutions per minute. If there is no slip between the belt and the pulley, then any point on the belt must move the same distance as any point on the circumference of the pulley. In one revolution this will be πd and in one minute it will be πdr. Similarly, if the diameter and speed of the follower pulley on the machine are D and R respectively, the distance moved by a point on the belt in one minute will be πDR. As both these distances

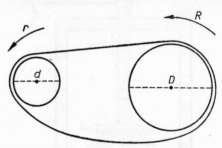

FIG. 6.12. MACHINE DRIVES IN PRINTING

are the distance moved by any point on the belt in one minute—

$$\pi dr = \pi DR$$

and so, $$dr = DR \qquad . \qquad . \qquad . \qquad . \qquad (12)$$

Therefore in any belt and pulley system the diameter and speed of the driving pulley multiplied together are equal to the diameter and speed of the follower pulley multiplied.

When the belt is replaced by a chain and the pulleys by sprockets the same argument applies, but it is sometimes difficult to find the effective diameter (pitch diameter) of a toothed wheel. This difficulty can be avoided by using the number of teeth on each sprocket instead of the diameter. You can use the same method to show that with chain drives—

$$\text{no. of teeth} \times \text{speed} = \text{no. of teeth} \times \text{speed} \qquad . \ (13)$$
$$\text{(driver)} \qquad\qquad\qquad \text{(follower)}$$

and that the same relationship applies for driver and follower when two gear wheels mesh together.

THINGS TO LEARN

1. Forces have both size and direction. They are compounded by using the parallelogram of forces.

2. Work done = force × distance moved in the direction of operation of the force.

3. Energy can be changed from one form to another but cannot be destroyed.

4. Power is the rate at which work is done or energy expended.

5. The characteristics of a machine are—

$$\text{mechanical advantage} = \frac{\text{load or resistance overcome}}{\text{effort applied}}$$

$$\text{velocity ratio} = \frac{\text{distance moved by effort}}{\text{distance moved by load}}$$

$$\text{efficiency} = \frac{\text{work done on load}}{\text{work done by effort}}$$

6. Pulley and gear ratios are—

$$\begin{array}{cc} \text{diameter} \times \text{speed} = \text{diameter} \times \text{speed} \\ \text{(driver)} \qquad \qquad \text{(follower)} \end{array}$$

$$\begin{array}{cc} \text{no. of teeth} \times \text{speed} = \text{no. of teeth} \times \text{speed} \\ \text{(driver)} \qquad \qquad \text{(follower)} \end{array}$$

OTHER BOOKS TO READ

L. S. POWELL, *Elementary Physics for Technical Students* (Pitman)
M. NELKON, *Principles of Physics* (Christophers)

EXERCISES

1. Show with diagrams what you understand by levers of the first, second, and third orders. Give as an example of each something you would expect to find in a printing works. (Lp Mc/1959/Int.)

2. A piece of brass rule needs a force of 120 lb wt. to cut it. If it is placed in a rule cutter at a distance of half an inch from the pivot and the lever handle is a foot long, what effort will be needed to cut the rule?

3. Explain what is meant by the terms: (a) mechanical advantage; (b) efficiency (of a machine); and (c) velocity ratio. Show how they are connected. (Lp Mc/1960/Int.)

4. Draw diagrams of two types of simple machine with a mechanical advantage of 4 in the absence of friction, giving the dimensions on the diagrams. How will friction in each case affect the efficiency of the machine?

5. What is the difference between work and power and in what units may each be measured? If a reel weighing 760 lb is hoisted to a height of 22 ft in 2 min how much work will be done and what is the minimum power needed for the motor of the hoist, ignoring friction?

6. A printing cylinder weighing 450 lb is lifted 2 ft by a chain-operated block and tackle. If the effort required on the chain is 50 lb wt. and the chain is pulled a distance of 28 ft what is the efficiency of the tackle?

7. A folding machine needs 5 revolutions of its pulley to complete operations on one sheet and will handle 2,500 sheets an hour. If the diameter of the machine pulley is 12 in., what size pulley will be required on a 500 r.p.m. motor used to power the machine?

8. Describe three methods of driving a printing press and list the advantages and disadvantages of each. (Lp Mc 1960/Fin.)

CHAPTER 7

MAKING USE OF PRESSURE

WHEN a forme of type is rested on its corner on a wooden surface it will make a dent in the wood, but if it is laid down flat it will make no dent, although its weight is just the same as before. If the weight of the forme is 25 lb then in both cases the force acting on the wood is 25 lb wt., but in the first case the force acted on a very small area and in the second over the whole area of the forme, say 100 sq. in. We say the *pressure* was lower when the forme was flat. Pressure is the force exerted on unit area, so if the forme corner was in contact with one square inch of wood the pressure would be 25 lb wt. per square inch compared with only 0·25 lb wt. per square inch when the forme was flat. The average pressure p on a surface is—

$$p = \frac{\text{total force on the surface } (F)}{\text{area of surface } (A)} \qquad . \qquad . \quad (1)$$

and the total force on a surface is given by—

$$F = pA \qquad . \qquad . \qquad . \quad (2)$$

So if we wish to place a book under a pressure of 10 lb wt. per sq. in. and the area of the book is 40 sq. in. then we have to apply a total force of 400 lb wt.

Pressure in Fluids. If we take a wide glass tube and cover the ends with thin balloon rubber, the rubber will be pressed inward as the tube is lowered into a tall glass jar of water. The deeper the tube goes the further the rubber is pressed in because the pressure of the water increases with depth (Fig. 7.1). It should also be noted that the rubber is pressed inward to the same extent at any given depth at whatever angle the tube lies. This is because the pressure in a fluid acts equally in every direction.

To find the pressure at any depth in a fluid we imagine

column of the fluid resting on a base of unit area, as in Fig. 7.2. The pressure on the area will be the weight of the column resting on it. If the height of the column is h, the volume of

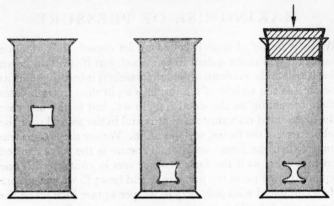

FIG. 7.1. INCREASE OF PRESSURE WITH DEPTH

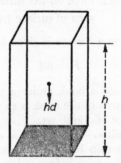

FIG. 7.2. FINDING THE PRESSURE OF A FLUID

the column will be h (cubic feet or centimetres according to the system of units) and its weight hd, where d is the density of the fluid. Thus the pressure at any point in a fluid is given by—

$$p = hd \qquad . \qquad . \qquad . \qquad (3)$$

Hydraulic Press. When the top of the jar in Fig. 7.1 is closed by a cork, it will be found that any pressure on the cork will be transmitted through the water to press the rubber still further into the ends of the tube. Transmission of pressure through a fluid is used to obtain the large forces needed for

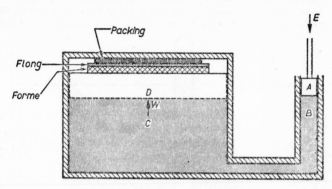

FIG. 7.3. THE HYDRAULIC PRESS

moulding stereo- and electro-typing matrices, for some makes of guillotine and for baling presses.

The principle of the hydraulic press is shown in Fig. 7.3. The small piston A is acted upon by a force of, say, 40 lb wt. and transmits pressure to the fluid in tube B. If the area of this tube is 5 sq. in. then the pressure exerted on the fluid will be 8 lb wt. per sq. in. This pressure is transmitted by the fluid to the large cylinder C and the tight-fitting piston D, which we will assume to have an area of 500 sq. in. The force W exerted by D on the forme and flong above it will be 8×500 lb wt., that is, 4,000 lb wt. or 100 times the effort applied. As the pressure on the small piston is $\dfrac{E}{a}$ and that on the large piston $\dfrac{W}{A}$ and these are equal, we see that for any such system mechanical advantage $= \dfrac{W}{E} = \dfrac{A}{a}$.   . (4)

Atmospheric Pressure. As we live at the bottom of an ocean of air which we call the atmosphere it is only to be expected that it will exert pressure on us all the time.

EXPERIMENT 1. TO FIND THE PRESSURE OF THE ATMOSPHERE

Apparatus. Mercury trough; mercury; long glass tube; meter rule.

Take a glass tube about 3 ft long and seal it at one end. Carefully fill the tube with mercury so that no air is left in it and invert it in a trough

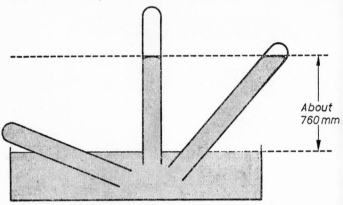

About
760 mm

FIG. 7.4. MERCURY REGISTERING ATMOSPHERIC PRESSURE

filled with mercury. Measure the height above the level of the mercury in the trough at which the mercury in the tube comes to rest. Repeat with the tube at different angles.

In the above experiment it will be found that the mercury in the tube always stands about 760 mm vertically above the level of the mercury in the trough as shown in Fig. 7.4. The height of the mercury column, in fact, just balances the pressure of the air on the surface of the mercury in the trough. You can work out what this pressure is by using eqn. 3—the answer will be about 14·5 lb per sq. in. This is the normal pressure exerted by the atmosphere which varies slightly from time to time. By measuring these changes with a *barometer*, which is a tube of mercury like that used in the experiment, some idea can be obtained of how the weather is likely to change.

AIR PRESSURE APPLIED

The printing frames used in the photomechanical departments
of printing works use atmospheric pressure to get firm contact
between the negative or positive and the light-sensitive coating
when the photographic image is being printed down on the
metal. The two are placed as the inside of a sandwich between
a glass cover and a backboard which are squeezed together

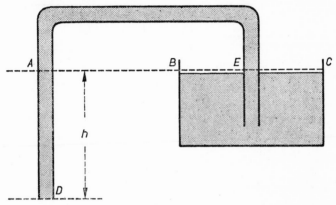

Fig. 7.5

by the pressure of the atmosphere as the air in the sandwich
is removed by a vacuum pump. Suction fingers on feeding
mechanisms operate by reducing the pressure inside the finger
so that the higher pressure outside holds the sheet of paper
against the finger, which releases it when the pressure inside
is again made equal to or greater than the pressure outside.

Siphon. Baths and tanks are sometimes emptied by putting
into them one end of a tube filled with liquid and holding the
other end below the level of the container, as in Fig. 7.5. The
pressure in the liquid at surface level, along the line ABC, will
be the pressure of the atmosphere. At the end of the tube D
the upward pressure is also the pressure of the atmosphere, but
the downward pressure will be the pressure of the atmosphere
plus the pressure due to the column of liquid AD, which will

be *hd*, where *d* is the density of the liquid. The liquid will therefore run out of the tube. Notice that if *D* is above the level of the liquid in the container there will be no flow and that

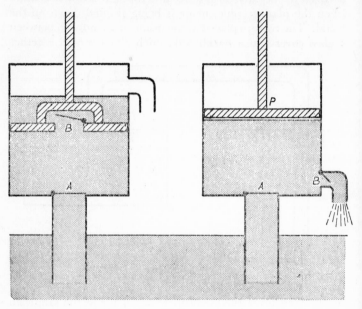

FIG. 7.6. TWO SIMPLE TYPES OF PUMP

if the tube is empty the atmospheric pressure will not be able to raise the liquid above the point *E*.

Pumps. All pumps make use of pressure in some way for their operation. Two simple types of pump are shown in Fig. 7.6. In the lift pump on the left, which is the type used on some stereotyping machines, the pressure of the atmosphere forces liquid through the valve *A* as the piston *P* rises. This liquid then passes through the valve *B* as the piston descends, and is pushed from the outlet as the piston rises again. In the force pump (right) liquid is lifted by the up stroke and forced through the valve *B* by the down stroke.

THINGS TO LEARN

1. Pressure is the force acting on unit area.
2. Pressure in a liquid or gas acts equally in all directions.
3. Pressure in a liquid = depth × density.
4. Atmospheric pressure is about 14 lb wt. per sq. in.

OTHER BOOKS TO READ

As previous Chapter.

EXERCISES

1. Explain the difference between the weight of an object and the pressure exerted by its base on the supports. If a machine weighing one ton has two bearers each 3 ft long by 3 in. wide what pressure in lb per sq. in. will it exert on the floor?

2. A moulding press is required to exert an average pressure of 10 lb per sq. in. on the face of a forme measuring 20 in. by 30 in. What will be the total force exerted by the press?

3. Compressive force of 12,000 lb wt. has to be exerted to bale-up waste paper by a hydraulic baling machine which has an effective area of 150 sq. in. for the ram. What force must be exerted on the pumping piston of ¼ sq. in. cross-sectional area.

4. Draw a diagram showing the principle of operation of a hydraulic press. If the ram of the press has an area of 96 sq. in. and the inlet pipe is ⅛ sq. in. area of cross-section, what is the mechanical advantage given by the press?

CHAPTER 8

FLUIDS ON THE MOVE

MOST of us must have noticed when called upon to help with the washing-up that water breaks up into small round drops on a greasy plate but spreads out into a thin even film on a clean one. In the latter case we say the water has wetted the plate. The ability of a liquid to wet one surface but not another is the whole basis of lithographic printing. It is also important in determining whether one ink will take on another in the absorption of adhesives, oil and water by paper and in the fly of ink from rotating plates and rollers.

Surface Tension. The water on a greasy surface rolls up into drops because all liquids behave as though they are surrounded by a thin skin or membrane trying to hold them together. The formation of a drop of water on the end of a dripping tap can be imitated by covering the end of the tap with a piece of balloon rubber (Fig. 8.1) and letting the rubber slowly fill with water. As the rubber fills it will stretch and form a neck just like a drop of water about to fall. It does not fall because the tension in the rubber increases as it stretches, while with a liquid the tension of the apparent skin remains the same and the drop falls when the pull of gravity exceeds the pull of the "skin."

No such skin does, in fact, exist but the forces of attraction between the molecules of the liquid create a skinlike effect which we call *surface tension*. The molecules behave rather like a crowd of people gathered round a street fight. Everyone presses closer in to get a good view and the "drop" of people formed becomes circular. If you try to elbow your way in you have to overcome the resistance due to the fact that everyone else is pressing toward the centre—in other words the crowd has a kind of surface tension. This resistance will be greater with a crowd made up of rugby forwards than with one made up of children.

As the fight surges near a wall the "drop" of people tends to spread out because there is no difficulty about leaning against the wall to watch. On the other hand, when the fight gets near a barbed wire fence the people try to avoid being pushed on the wire and the crowd rolls along the fence like a drop of water on a greasy plate.

When a liquid is in contact with a solid surface there are three kinds of surface tension to be taken into account—between liquid and solid, between liquid and air, and between

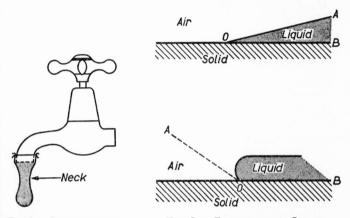

FIG. 8.1. DEMONSTRATION OF SURFACE TENSION

FIG. 8.2. EQUILIBRIUM OF SURFACE TENSION FORCES

air and solid. These three forces will reach equilibrium at various angles as shown in Fig. 8.2. For the liquid to wet the surface and spread completely over it the angle AOB must be zero. As this angle increases the ability of the liquid to wet the surface decreases until the angle becomes so large that the liquid breaks up into droplets, like printing ink refusing to take on a previously printed colour.

The function of wetting agents used in the printing and allied trades is to adjust the surface tension to a value which allows the spread of liquid over a surface. Any surface which needs to be wetted should be thoroughly cleaned as the presence of very small quantities of grease can interfere with the uniformity of damping, etching and other processes.

Capillary Attraction. When two glass plates, touching at one edge and held slightly apart at the other, are dipped into a liquid it will be found that the liquid will climb up the

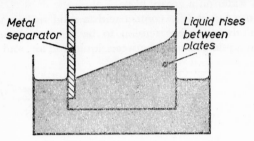

FIG. 8.3. CAPILLARY ATTRACTION

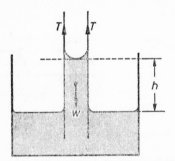

FIG. 8.4. MEASURING SURFACE TENSION BY MEANS OF A CAPILLARY TUBE

gap between the plates (Fig. 8.3). The final level of the liquid will be higher where the plates are close together than where they are farther apart. In the same way a number of fine-bore (capillary) tubes placed in a liquid will cause it to rise in them to a height which is proportional to the surface tension of the liquid and inversely proportional to the diameter of the tube. This capillary attraction, which is due to surface tension, is responsible for the absorption of liquids by sponges, paper,

and other porous materials. Surface tension of a liquid can
be measured by means of a capillary tube. From Fig. 8.4 it
can be seen that the upward force on the column of liquid is
$2\pi r T$, where T is the surface tension per centimetre of the
line of contact between the liquid and the tube, and r is the
radius. Acting downward will be the weight of the column
$\pi r^2 hdg$, where h is the height, d the density, and g the gravitational constant. The liquid will stop rising when these two
forces become equal, that is, when

$$2\pi r T = \pi r^2 hdg$$

therefore $$T = \tfrac{1}{2}rhdg \quad . \quad . \quad . \quad . \quad (1)$$

the value of T being in dynes per centimetre when measurements are made in metric units.

EXPERIMENT 1. TO FIND THE SURFACE TENSION OF A LIQUID

Apparatus. Glass vessel; fine capillary tube; travelling microscope.

Holding the capillary tube upright, dip one end deeply into the liquid.
Raise the tube slightly so that it is wetted properly round the meniscus and
fix in a vertical position in the field of view of the microscope. This is used
to measure the height h (Fig. 8.4) by first focusing on the surface of the
liquid in the container and then on the meniscus in the tube. Cut the tube
at the level reached by the liquid and measure the diameter with a travelling
microscope or a microscope fitted with an eyepiece scale. The surface
tension can then be determined from eqn. 1, the result being in dynes per
centimetre if the measurements are made in centimetres.

It is useful to repeat this experiment with a series of liquids
to compare their surface tensions and to use it to study the
effect of wetting agents.

When paper is made there are always spaces between the
fibres and between the fibres and particles of loading to act
as capillary tubes drawing the liquid part of the ink into the
body of the paper. The fibres themselves are also fine capillary
tubes. The number and size of these openings or "pores" will
determine the oil-absorption speed of the paper.

Resistance to Flow. The speed at which various liquids
will flow up the tube in the experiment above will vary very
widely. Water, for instance, will reach the highest point more
quickly than a linseed-oil varnish. This difference in speed is

due to the differing resistances of the liquids to the forces trying to move them. Resistance to flow is known as *viscosity* and it plays a major part in determining how ink, varnishes, adhesives and other fluids behave in printing and subsequent processes.

In some liquids flow begins however small the force applied, while in others flow will not begin until the force reaches a certain minimum value. The difference can be seen by placing a few drops of water and a little printing ink on two clean microscope slides. The water will begin to spread immediately but the ink will not flow until the slide is tilted sufficiently for the force of gravity acting on it to reach the required value to start the flow. The type of flow which takes place under any force is known as *Newtonian flow* and that which requires a minimum force to start it is called *plastic flow*.

By mixing increasing amounts of some insoluble solid such as powdered chalk with a liquid it can be seen that the resistance to flow increases. This fact is of considerable importance in printing inks which are essentially a mixture of solid pigment particles with a liquid. The solid particles tend to build up a structure which still further impedes the flow of the ink but which breaks down when the ink is stirred vigorously. The property of building up a very high resistance to flow on standing is known as *thixotropy*.

Comparing Viscosities. As the flow of an ink or adhesive will affect its distribution on a machine and its rate of penetration into paper or board, we sometimes need to compare the rate of flow of one sample with another. This comparison can be made with instruments called *viscometers*. The first group of these depends on the time taken for a fixed volume of liquid to flow through a narrow tube or orifice. Typical of them are the Ostwald viscometer and the Ford cup (Fig. 8.5). The Ostwald viscometer is used for comparing the time taken for samples of the liquids drawn into the bulb *A* to empty under the force of gravity through the capillary tube immediately below it. The time recorded is that between the upper level of the liquid passing the marks *C* and *D*. The second bulb *B* acts as a reservoir for the discharged liquid. An average of several readings, all taken at the same temperature is required. This type of viscometer is made with different-sized tubes to suit a wide range of viscosities. Ford cups, also made with different sizes of aperture, are exactly filled to

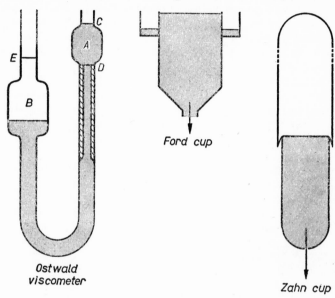

Ford cup

Ostwald
viscometer

Zahn cup

FIG. 8.5.　THREE TYPES OF VISCOMETER

the top, an overflow ring being provided to take any excess scraped off the top. When the cup is full the time taken for it to empty through the aperture in the bottom is taken and can be compared with the time taken by another liquid. The cup is regarded as being empty when the thread of liquid flowing out first breaks.

Although either method is suitable for use with an un-pigmented vehicle, neither will give reliable results with a printing ink. For workshop use comparison can be made between the flow rates of low-viscosity inks such as those used in high-speed gravure by means of the Zahn cup (Fig. 8.5).

Held by its long handle the cup is immersed in the ink duct and the time taken for it to empty is compared with standard times already established as satisfactory for the type of work in hand.

Another type of instrument times the fall of a heavy body through a sample of the liquid under test. Shown in Fig. 8.6

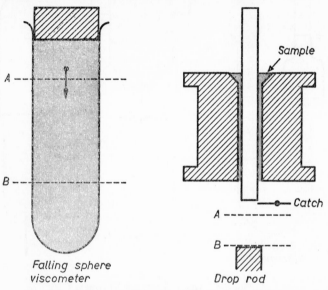

Falling sphere viscometer

Sample

Catch

Drop rod

FIG. 8.6. TIMING THE FALL OF A HEAVY BODY THROUGH
A SAMPLE OF LIQUID

are two examples, the falling sphere viscometer, suitable for unpigmented vehicles, and the drop rod, used for very viscous inks such as are used on letterpress or lithographic machines. The former is also used for measuring viscosity of adhesives. In the case of the falling-sphere instrument, which may be a corked test tube for rough and ready tests, a steel ball bearing is allowed to reach a steady speed and the time it takes to pass from A to B is measured. The drop rod is moved up and down several times in the metal bobbin to break down the thixotropy of the ink and to ensure its even distribution over the rod. The time the rod takes to fall at steady speed from A to B is taken.

Perhaps the most useful type of viscometer for the printing trade is the rotational type, the principle of which is illustrated in Fig. 8.7. The outer cylinder is rotated by a motor and

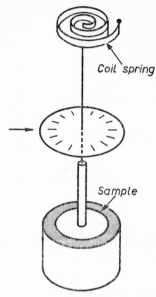

Coil spring

Sample

FIG. 8.7. THE ROTATIONAL TYPE OF VISCOMETER

exerts a drag on the inner cylinder which is suspended from a torsion wire or spring. The deflexion of the scale attached to the wire is proportional to the drag, which depends on the viscosity of the sample between the two cylinders. Any thixotropy of the sample is allowed for by waiting for the deflexion to fall to a steady value. The instrument also allows for changes in viscosity with rate of shear by having a motor with variable speed of rotation. It can reproduce more closely the conditions which actually obtain on a given machine.

In its portable form the rotational type of viscometer can be used in the machine room or bindery to measure flow properties of ink in the duct or adhesive in the tank.

Effect of Temperature. All viscosity measurements should be carried out in carefully controlled temperature conditions. Viscosity varies very considerably with temperature as any machine printer who has started up in a cold machine

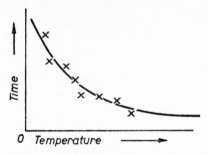

FIG. 8.8. GRAPH SHOWING THE TIME OF FLOW AGAINST TEMPERATURE

room will have found by experience. As the temperature rises the viscosity falls, an increase of 20°F reducing the viscosity of some liquids to a half or even a third of the former value.

EXPERIMENT 2. TO FIND HOW VISCOSITY VARIES WITH TEMPERATURE

Apparatus. Ostwald viscometer; water jacket; stop watch; thermometer.
Place a suitable liquid, such as mineral oil, in the viscometer which should be lowered into the water jacket (a large beaker will serve) until the water is above the upper mark on the viscometer. Put a little ice into the water to bring it below room temperature and when a steady thermometer reading has been reached time the flow of the liquid through the capillary tube. Slowly warm the water to about 50°C, taking flow times at regular intervals. Draw a graph showing the time of flow against the temperature. A curve of the general shape of Fig. 8.8. should be obtained. Repeat for number of other liquids.

Problems of flow of ink and adhesives are very complex and we have been able only to skirt the fringes of them in this short chapter. Attempts are now being made to secure automatic control of the flow of inks to improve consistency of colour reproduction in high-speed printing and it is well worth following some of the articles on this question which appear from time to time in the technical press.

THINGS TO LEARN

1. Surface tension is the force which acts on the vehicle of a printing ink and causes it to be drawn into the spaces between fibres and loading of paper.

2. Viscosity is the resistance to flow of a liquid. It is increased by the addition of solid particles and reduced by a rise in temperature.

3. Thixotropy is the formation of a particle structure in a pigmented vehicle causing the mixture to show an increase in resistance to flow after standing.

OTHER BOOKS TO READ

E. N. DA C. ANDRADE, *Viscosity and Plasticity* (Oil and Colour Chemists Assn.)

R. S. BURDON, *Surface Tension and the Spreading of Liquids* (Cambridge University Press)

J. K. VENNARD, *Elementary Fluid Mechanics* (Wiley)

EXERCISES

1. What is thixotropy? Explain how it affects the flow of a letterpress or lithographic printing ink.

2. A gravure ink takes 65 sec to flow out of a Zahn cup on a cold day and only 50 sec on a warm day. With the aid of a diagram explain why this happens.

3. Describe how you would compare the viscosity of two varnishes using a test tube and a ball bearing.

4. You want to check that the adhesive in the tank of a gluing machine conforms to the viscosity required for the job in progress. Describe the principle of operation of an instrument suitable for this purpose.

5. Explain why it is important that metal surfaces should be thoroughly cleaned before etching.

CHAPTER 9

CHEMICAL TYPES

Metals and Non-metals. It is usually quite easy to distinguish a metal from a non-metal. We expect metals to be hard dense materials with what we call a metallic lustre. They are usually malleable, which means that they are tough and can be rolled or hammered into thin sheets. Many of them are ductile or capable of being drawn into fine wire and generally they are good conductors of heat and electricity. On the other hand we expect non-metals to have none of these properties and we are usually, but not always, right.

It is not difficult to find exceptions to the simple rules shown in Table 4. For instance, mercury with a melting

Table 4

THE PHYSICAL PROPERTIES OF METALS AND NON-METALS

Metals	Non-metals
e.g. Copper, silver, gold, platinum, lead, tin, antimony, aluminium, magnesium, zinc, potassium, iron, sodium	e.g. Hydrogen, oxygen, nitrogen, chlorine, bromine, iodine, carbon, sulphur, phosphorus, helium, neon
Metallic lustre (may tarnish)	No metallic lustre
High density	Low density
Hard and high tensile strength	Soft, low tensile strength
Malleable and ductile	Brittle
Metallic sound when struck	No metallic sound when struck
Good conductors of heat	Poor conductors of heat
Good conductors of electricity	Poor conductors of electricity
Usually solids	Gases, liquids or low melting solids

point of −39°C and therefore a liquid at ordinary temperatures could hardly be beaten into sheets or drawn into wire. Sodium is a soft metal with a density of only 0·97 gm per c.c. and the non-metal carbon in the form of diamonds is one of the hardest materials known. Metals and non-metals are much more clearly divided by their chemical properties, as we shall see when we come to consider their oxides.

CLASSES OF CHEMICAL COMPOUNDS

We have seen how the 102 elements can be put into two classes, metals and non-metals, but, as you can imagine, it is a different matter to try and classify more than a million compounds. Over 90 per cent of these chemicals are compounds of the element carbon with other elements. They are known as *organic compounds* and their study as *organic chemistry*. A great many of our modern materials including drugs, plastics, insecticides, and the solvents, resins, and most of the pigments used in printing inks are synthetic organic compounds. Compounds of the elements other than carbon are called *inorganic* compounds and the study of these chemicals is known as *inorganic chemistry*.

The four most common groups of inorganic compounds are—

Oxides
Acids
Bases
Salts.

Oxides. If you hold a piece of magnesium ribbon with a pair of tongs in a bunsen flame the metal soon begins to burn with a brilliant white flame. The white solid that is formed in the reaction is magnesium oxide. Similarly, if you heat some sulphur in air it burns with a bluish flame and the gas sulphur dioxide is given off. The combination of any element with oxygen gives what is called an *oxide*. A metal often combines with oxygen in the air to form a layer of oxide on its surface. The chemical properties of the oxides of the elements provide an important difference between metals and non-metals.

8—(T.940)

EXPERIMENT 1. TO INVESTIGATE THE PROPERTIES OF VARIOUS OXIDES

Heat a small quantity of sulphur in a deflagrating spoon (Fig. 9.1) and when it begins to burn transfer it to a gas jar of oxygen (or less satisfactorily air). Note the appearance of the oxide formed, remove the spoon, add a little distilled water and shake up the jar to see if the oxide will dissolve.

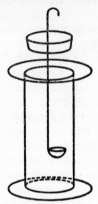

FIG. 9.1. A DEFLAGRATING SPOON

Test the solution with a drop of litmus. Litmus goes red with acids and blue with alkalis.

Repeat the experiment with magnesium, carbon, iron filings, and sodium. (*Note.* Sodium is extremely reactive and is kept under oil.)

Summarize the results in a table. (Table 5.)

Table 5

Element	Appearance of Oxide	Solubility of Oxide	Colour of Litmus
Sulphur	colourless gas choking fumes	soluble	red
Magnesium	white solid	partly soluble	blue
Carbon	colourless gas	soluble	red
Iron	grey solid	insoluble	—
Sodium	white solid	soluble	blue

The above experiment will show that—

(i) The oxides of the non-metals used were gases which dissolved in water to give acidic solutions.

(ii) The oxides of the metals used, when soluble, gave alkaline solutions.

The oxides (and hydroxides) of the metals are called bases. Some bases dissolve in water to form an alkali. A solution of an oxide of a non-metal is called an acid, e.g.

Magnesium oxide + water = Magnesium hydroxide (BASE)
    (Magnesia)

Calcium oxide + water = Calcium hydroxide (BASE)
    (Quicklime)   (Slaked lime)

Carbon dioxide + water = Carbonic acid

Sulphur trioxide + water = Sulphuric acid

Acids. Among the chemicals used in the printing industry are several acids including: sulphuric acid, hydrochloric acid, nitric acid, phosphoric acid, chromic acid, and acetic acid.

Most acids have certain characteristic properties.

(i) Their solutions turn litmus red.

(ii) They usually taste sour in dilute solutions, e.g. lemons (citric), vinegar (acetic), grapes (tartaric), and sour milk (lactic).

(iii) They react with certain metals to give a salt, e.g. zinc + hydrochloric acid = zinc chloride + hydrogen gas.

(iv) They are neutralized by the oxides (and hydroxides) of metals, i.e. *bases* to give a salt and water only.

ACID + BASE = SALT + WATER.

e.g. Hydrochloric acid + Sodium hydroxide (caustic soda) = Sodium chloride (common salt) + water

Hydrochloric acid + Copper oxide = Copper chloride + water

Bases. From our point of view the soluble bases or alkalis are the most important chemicals in this group. Alkalis that are in common use in the industry are: sodium hydroxide (caustic soda), potassium hydroxide (caustic potash), and ammonium hydroxide.

Like acids, most alkalis have certain characteristic properties, as follows—

(i) Their solutions turn litmus blue.

(ii) They have a "caustic" action on the skin and their dilute solutions have a "soapy" feel and taste.

(iii) They do not attack metals, with a very few exceptions including zinc and aluminium.

(iv) They are neutralized by acids to give a salt and water only (*see* properties of acids).

EXPERIMENT 2. TO EXAMINE THE PROPERTIES OF ACIDS AND ALKALIS

1. *Their Effect on Litmus and Other Indicators*

(*a*) Add about 4 drops of concentrated hydrochloric acid to 50 ml of water in a 100-ml beaker. Stir with a glass rod and pour the solution into three test tubes so that each is about one-third full. Add a few drops of litmus to the first solution (goes red), a similar amount of phenolphthalein to the second (colourless) and methyl orange to the third (red). Finally, add concentrated sodium hydroxide slowly to each solution until there is a colour change. The solutions will now be blue, red, and orange respectively.

(*b*) Add about 4 drops of concentrated sodium hydroxide to 50 ml of water in a 100-ml beaker. Stir, then pour the solution into three test tubes so that each is approximately one-third full. Add a few drops of litmus to the first solution (blue), phenolphthalein to the second (red) and methyl orange to the third (orange). Slowly add concentrated hydrochloric acid to each solution until a colour change takes place. The solutions will now be red, colourless, and red respectively.

2. *Their Effect on Metals*

Place a small quantity of iron filings in each of two test tubes. Add sufficient dilute hydrochloric acid to one of these tubes to just cover the metal. A reaction takes place in which bubbles of gas form on the surface of the metal. If necessary warm. (*N.B.* Most chemical reactions take place more rapidly as the temperature is increased.) Testing with a lighted splint will show that this gas is hydrogen. To the second test tube add a similar quantity of sodium hydroxide. There is no visible reaction.

Repeat the experiment using the metals copper, aluminium, zinc, and magnesium. If the reaction with dilute hydrochloric is going very slowly in the cold, try adding a few drops of concentrated acid to your solution. (*N.B.* Most chemical reactions in solution go faster when the reagents are more concentrated.)

3. *Their Effect upon Each Other, i.e. Neutralization*

Add a solution of sodium hydroxide to an evaporating dish so that it is about one-quarter full. A drop of the solution taken out on a glass rod and spotted on to litmus paper will turn it blue. Slowly add hydrochloric acid of similar strength to the alkali, testing a spot of the mixture on litmus paper after each addition. When the paper turns red add more sodium hydroxide a drop at a time until the paper just turns blue. Now add one drop of hydrochloric acid. The solution is now very close to the *neutral point*, where the acid and the alkali are equally balanced. Evaporate the solution to dryness and examine the product. Its taste should be familiar. Two corrosive chemicals have reacted together to form the harmless sodium chloride (common salt).

$$\text{Hydrochloric acid} + \text{Sodium hydroxide} = \text{Sodium chloride} + \text{water}$$

$$\text{ACID} + \text{BASE} = \text{SALT} + \text{WATER}$$

Repeat the experiment with other pairs of acids and bases, e.g.

Potassium hydroxide + Dilute sulphuric acid.

Ammonium hydroxide + Dilute hydrochloric acid.

Copper oxide + Sulphuric acid (add the black copper oxide to dilute sulphuric until some is left undissolved, filter, evaporate to small bulk and leave to crystallize).

Salts. There are far more salts than there are acids and bases and many of these occur in nature. We have already seen that a salt is produced when an acid neutralizes a base, e.g.

$$\text{Potassium hydroxide} + \text{Hydrochloric acid} = \text{Potassium chloride} + \text{water}$$

$$\text{Magnesium oxide} + \text{Sulphuric acid} = \text{Magnesium sulphate} + \text{water}$$

and when an acid attacks a metal, e.g.

$$\text{Zinc} + \frac{\text{Hydrochloric}}{\text{acid}} = \frac{\text{Zinc}}{\text{chloride}} + \frac{\text{Hydrogen}}{\text{gas}}$$

$$\text{Magnesium} + \frac{\text{Sulphuric}}{\text{acid}} = \frac{\text{Magnesium}}{\text{sulphate}} + \frac{\text{Hydrogen}}{\text{gas}}$$

There are other methods of preparing salts, as described in Chapter 16.

The name of a salt can tell us quite a lot about its composition. The name has two parts: the first part is a metal (or ammonium) derived from a base, and the second part from the acid, which reacts with the base to form the particular salt. Those salts with the ending -ate contain oxygen, those ending -ite contain less oxygen (e.g. sulphites contain less oxygen than sulphates) and those ending -ide contain no oxygen.

Hydrochloric acid gives a series of chloride salts
Hydrocyanic acid   ,,   ,,   ,,   ,, cyanide salts
Nitric acid   ,,   ,,   ,,   ,, nitrate salts
Phosphoric acid   ,,   ,,   ,,   ,, phosphate salts
Acetic acid   ,,   ,,   ,,   ,, acetate salts
Oxalic acid   ,,   ,,   ,,   ,, oxalate salts
Carbonic acid   ,,   ,,   ,,   ,, carbonate salts
Sulphuric acid   ,,   ,,   ,,   ,, sulphate salts
Sulphurous acid   ,,   ,,   ,,   ,, sulphite salts

Most salts are crystalline materials which dissolve in water. Their solutions are not necessarily neutral but may be acidic or alkalinic (Hydrolysis, Chapter 15).

SOLUTION

If you add a little powdered copper sulphate to some water it will soon dissolve to give a blue *solution*. A solution is a very fine uniform mixture of two or more substances. We refer to the dissolved substance as the *solute*. Although in our example the solute is a solid, copper sulphate, in other solutions it might be a liquid or a gas, e.g. hydrochloric acid is a solution of hydrogen chloride gas in water, "fizzy" lemonade is largely a solution of the gas carbon dioxide in water, and methylated spirit is mainly a solution of water in alcohol.

The substance which does the dissolving, normally a liquid, is called the *solvent*. This is usually water but there are hundreds of other solvents, e.g. xylol is the solvent commonly used for gravure inks, white spirit is the solvent in paints, carbon tetrachloride is an excellent solvent for oils and fats.

To return to our copper sulphate, if we go on adding it to the solution we will reach a point where no more will dissolve. The solution is now said to be *saturated* at that temperature. Although salts will usually dissolve in water they are not all equally soluble. For instance sodium dichromate is over 30 times as soluble as potassium dichromate at 0°C. It follows that a solution of potassium dichromate is saturated more quickly than one of sodium dichromate. For convenience, the solubility of a substance may be expressed as a number, and we define it as *the maximum weight of the substance in grammes which will dissolve in* 100 *gm of the solvent at a given temperature and pressure* and in the presence of excess of the undissolved substance. If we speak of the solubility of sodium chloride in water being 37 at 20°C we mean that a solution of 37 gm of sodium chloride in 100 gm of water at 20°C is saturated.

Solubility and Temperature. If we warmed a cold saturated solution of copper sulphate we would find that more of the solid could now be dissolved. In fact, at boiling point we would find that the solubility of the salt had been increased five times. The solubility of a substance almost always increases with the temperature of the solvents (Fig. 9.2).

If a saturated solution at boiling point is cooled, the solvent is no longer able to hold the solute in solution and *crystallization* begins to take place. Crystals consist of regular patterns of atoms in space. The crystals of a particular salt have a definite geometrical form, but often the crystallizing conditions are such that large single crystals are unable to form. The best results are obtained when the solution is cooled slowly, free of dust with a small well-shaped crystal of the solute suspended in the solution to act as a nucleus on which atoms can build.

EXPERIMENT 3. TO PREPARE A LARGE CRYSTAL OF COPPER SULPHATE

Prepare a warm saturated solution of copper sulphate, cool, filter, and pour into a beaker. Suspend a small well-shaped crystal of the salt in the middle of the solution by means of a thread. Cover the beaker with a piece

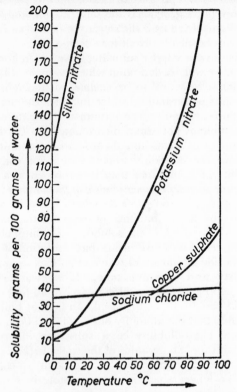

FIG. 9.2. SOLUBILITY AND TEMPERATURE

of card or paper to reduce the entry of dust and draught. Leave for some days in a cool still place.

Water of Crystallization. When some salts crystallize out of water solutions they carry into their crystals a certain number of molecules of water. This water is known as "*water of crystallization*" and the salt is said to be a *hydrate* or *hydrated*.

The familiar crystals of washing soda are a hydrated form of sodium carbonate. Their formula is $Na_2CO_3 \cdot 10H_2O$ and almost two-thirds of their weight is water of crystallization. Sodium carbonate can also be obtained as a powder which contains no water of crystallization. This is known as the *anhydrous* form of a salt. Although the two forms of a salt will behave chemically in exactly the same way, an equal weight of the anhydrous form will give a much greater effect since it is always more concentrated than the hydrate.

Say that you were making up a developing solution, whose formula specified 130 gm of sodium carbonate crystals ($Na_2CO_3 \cdot 10H_2O$) and all that you had available was the anhydrous sodium carbonate (Na_2CO_3). To give the right effect a much smaller amount of the powder must be added. Exactly what this amount should be can be calculated in the following way. (It would be helpful to read the first section of the next chapter before attempting this calculation.)

Atomic weights—

$$Na = 23; \quad C = 12; \quad O = 16; \quad H = 1.$$

Molecular weight of anhydrous sodium carbonate—

$$Na_2CO_3 \; (see \text{ Chapter } 9) = (2 \times 23) + 12 + (3 \times 16)$$
$$= 46 + 12 + 48 = 106$$

Molecular weight of hydrated sodium carbonate—

$$Na_2CO_3 \cdot 10H_2O$$
$$= (2 \times 23) + 12 + (3 \times 16) + 10(2 \times 1 + 16)$$
$$= 46 + 12 + 48 + 10(18) = 106 + 180 = 286$$

286 gm of hydrate is equivalent to 106 gm of the anhydrous form.

1 gm of hydrate is equivalent to $\dfrac{106}{286}$ gm of the anhydrous form.

130 gm of hydrate is equivalent to $\dfrac{106}{286} \times 130$ gm of the anhydrous form

$$= 48 \cdot 2 \text{ gm of the anhydrous form.}$$

48·2 gm of anhydrous sodium carbonate will give the same effect as 130 gm of the hydrated crystals of sodium carbonate.

Many of the salts used in printing processes and particularly in photo-mechanical processes form hydrates, e.g.

> Sodium thiosulphate ("hypo"), $Na_2S_2O_3 \cdot 5H_2O$
> Ferrous sulphate, $FeSO_4 \cdot 7H_2O$
> Sodium sulphite, $Na_2SO_3 \cdot 7H_2O$
> Sodium sulphide, $Na_2S \cdot 9H_2O$
> Potassium ferrocyanide, $K_4Fe(CN)_6 \cdot 3H_2O$
> Potash alum, $K_2SO_4 \cdot Al_2(SO_4)_3 \cdot 24H_2O$

Notice that the amount of water of crystallization in these crystals varies considerably and that alum has as many as 24 molecules of water combined with it. On the other hand there are numbers of salts which never form a hydrate, including sodium chloride, silver bromide, ammonium dichromate and all the common salts of potassium.

EXPERIMENTS ON WATER OF CRYSTALLIZATION

1. Place a few crystals of blue copper sulphate in a small test tube and warm over a Bunsen. The water of crystallization is driven off in the form of steam and the blue crystals are slowly converted to a white powder which is anhydrous copper sulphate. If water is added to this anhydrous form, it is converted back to the blue hydrate. This colour change is actually used in the laboratory as a test for water.

2. Weigh a clean dry crucible, add some powdered crystals of zinc sulphate and weigh again. Warm the crucible over a Bunsen until all the water appears to have been driven off. Allow to cool, weigh, then heat again for a few more minutes. Cool and reweigh. If this weight is the same as the last then all the water has been driven off. If it is not the same, continue heating, cooling, and weighing until two consecutive weights are identical. Calculate the percentage of water in the crystals and compare this figure with the percentage that you would expect from the formula $ZnSO_4 \cdot 7H_2O$. (*See* specimen results below.)

Weight of crucible = 8·35 gm

Weight of crucible + Zinc sulphate crystals = 13·30 gm

Weight of crucible + Zinc sulphate after heating (1) = 11·15 gm

(2) = 11·13 gm

(3) = 11·13 gm

Weight of zinc sulphate crystals = 4·95 gm

Weight of anhydrous zinc sulphate = 2·78 gm

Loss in weight = weight of combined water = 2·17 gm

Percentage of combined water = $\dfrac{2·17}{4·95} \times \dfrac{100}{1}$ = 43·9

From the formula $ZnSO_4 \cdot 7H_2O$ (Zn = 65, S = 32, O = 16, H = 1)
Molecular weight of hydrate = 65 + 32 + (4 × 16) + 7(2 × 1 + 16)
$$= 65 + 32 + 64 + 7(18)$$
$$= 161 + 126 = 287.$$
Molecular weight of anhydrous salt = 65 + 32 + (4 × 16) = 161

287 gm of the hydrate is equivalent to 161 gm of anhydrous, i.e 287 gm of hydrate contains 287 − 161 gm of water = 126 gm of water.

Percentage of water in the hydrate according to formula

$$= \dfrac{126}{287} \times \dfrac{100}{1} = 43·9 \text{ per cent}$$

Efflorescence. Some hydrated salts tend to lose part of their water of crystallization when they are exposed to the atmosphere. These salts are said to be *efflorescent*. When hypo crystals, which are almost transparent, are left exposed to the air a layer of white powder forms on the surface. This powder is the anhydrous form of the salt.

Deliquescence. Other materials show the reverse effect in that they tend to take up water from the atmosphere. These substances are called *hygroscopic*. If, like calcium chloride and sodium hydroxide, the water taken up is sufficient to dissolve the substance to form a saturated solution then they are called *deliquescent*.

THINGS TO LEARN

1. The elements can be divided into *metals* and *non-metals*.

2. The compound of an element with oxygen is called an *oxide*.

3. Metal oxides (or hydroxides) are called bases. If they dissolve in water their solutions are alkaline, turning litmus blue.

4. Non-metal oxides are often gases which dissolve in water to give solutions which are acidic, turning litmus red.

5. An *acid* is a substance containing hydrogen which may be replaced by a metal to form a salt. Most acids will turn litmus red, attack most metals and neutralize a base to form a salt and water.

6. An *alkali* is a soluble hydroxide of a metal. Alkalis will turn litmus blue, attack a very few metals and neutralize an acid to form a salt and water.

7. The *solubility* of a substance is defined as the maximum weight of the substance which will dissolve in 100 grammes of the solvent at a given temperature and pressure.

OTHER BOOKS TO READ

See Chapter 3.

EXERCISES

1. Name three distinguishing features between a metal and a non-metal.
(E and S/1959/Int.)

2. (*a*) Describe briefly the difference in chemical composition between acids, bases, and salts, giving not more than three examples of each. (*b*) Outline the more obvious properties of each of the examples you select.
(Photo/1959/Int.)

3. What are the features to distinguish: (*a*) elements from compounds; (*b*) acids from bases. (E and S/1958/Int.)

4. Explain briefly the meaning of: (*a*) acidic oxide; (*b*) neutralization; and (*c*) indicator.

5. (*a*) What is an acid? (*b*) Give the names and chemical formulae of three each of the following: (i) oxide, (ii) acid, (iii) salt.
(E and S/1959/Int)

6. Explain clearly the meaning of the words solute, solvent, and solution. Illustrate your answer with examples from the industry.

7. The solubility of ammonium dichromate is 89 at 30°C. What do you understand by this? What weight of this salt will dissolve in 250 gm of water at 30°C?

8. Define, giving an example, the meaning of "water of crystallization."
(Photo/1960/Int.)

9. Explain the term "water of crystallization." How many grammes of copper sulphate crystals $CuSO_4 \cdot 5H_2O$ are equivalent to one kilogram of the anhydrous form? (Atomic weights $Cu = 64$, $S = 32$, $O = 16$)

10. Describe an experiment to find the percentage of water of crystallization in a given sample of an hydrated salt.

11. Write notes to show the meaning of the following: (*a*) anhydrous; (*b*) saturated solution; (*c*) deliquescence; (*d*) efflorescence.

CHAPTER 10

CHEMICAL REACTIONS

"Hypo" is the chemical normally used for fixing a photographic image. Its chemical name is sodium thiosulphate and its formula is $Na_2S_2O_3$. In other words, it is a chemical compound of three elements, 2 atoms of sodium Na, 2 atoms of sulphur S and 3 atoms of oxygen O. How do we know this to be true? The atomic weights of these three elements are sodium 23, sulphur 32 and oxygen 16. This tells us that a sulphur atom is twice as heavy as an oxygen atom, so if analysis showed that a certain compound contained an equal percentage of oxygen and sulphur by weight we would know that there were twice as many oxygen atoms as there were sulphur atoms in that particular compound. This is a nice simple example but, in any compound, if we divide the percentage by weight of each element present by its atomic weight, we arrive at the relative numbers of each type of atom.

If we were to analyse some "hypo" powder we would find that it consisted of 29·1 per cent sodium, 40·5 per cent sulphur and 30·4 per cent oxygen by weight. Dividing by the atomic weights we get: Sodium $\dfrac{29\cdot1}{23} = 1\cdot26$; Sulphur $\dfrac{40\cdot5}{32} = 1\cdot26$; Oxygen $\dfrac{30\cdot4}{16} = 1\cdot90$.

Dividing by the smallest number, Sodium $\dfrac{1\cdot26}{1\cdot26} = 1\cdot0$; Sulphur $\dfrac{1\cdot26}{1\cdot26} = 1\cdot0$; Oxygen $\dfrac{1\cdot90}{1\cdot26} = 1\cdot5$.

Multiplying by two to bring all these to whole numbers, Sodium 2; Sulphur 2; Oxygen 3 and the formula of "hypo" is $Na_2S_2O_3$. So as well as being a useful chemical shorthand for a compound, a formula also tells us how much of each element is present in that compound.

If we add the atomic weights of all the atoms in a compound we obtain its molecular weight, e.g.

Molecular weight of "hypo"

$$Na_2S_2O_3 = (2 \times 23) + (2 \times 32) \times (3 \times 16)$$
$$= 46 + 64 + 48 = 158.$$

The molecular weight is the weight of one molecule of a substance compared with the weight of one-sixteenth of an atom of oxygen. The atomic weight of oxygen is 16. The molecular weight of sulphur dioxide gas, $SO_2 = 32 + (2 \times 16) = 64$, and so one molecule of SO_2 weighs four times as much as one atom of oxygen, e.g.

What weight of oxygen is contained in 8 gm of aluminium oxide, Al_2O_3?

Atomic weights   Aluminium $= 27$

                       Oxygen $= 16$

Molecular weight of

$$Al_2O_3 = (2 \times 27) + (3 \times 16)$$
$$= 54 + 48 = 102.$$

102 gm of Al_2O_3 contains 48 gm of oxygen

1 gm of Al_2O_3 contains $\frac{48}{102}$ gm of oxygen

8 gm of Al_2O_3 contains $\frac{48}{102} \times 8 = 3 \cdot 76$ gm of oxygen.

CHEMICAL EQUATIONS

A chemical equation is an extension of the chemical short-hand we have been using, to describe what happens in a chemical reaction. We will take as our example a reaction which is made use of in printing and try to write an equation to describe that reaction.

The layer of oxide which forms on a zinc plate can be removed by treating the plate with hydrochloric acid (a solution of hydrogen chloride gas in water).

In order to write the equation for this reaction we must

first write the formulae of the reacting substances. Analysis would show the formula of zinc oxide to be ZnO and hydrogen chloride HCl. These formulae could also be worked out from a knowledge of the valencies of the elements present (Chapter 3). The valency of both zinc and oxygen is two, so the formula of zinc oxide must be ZnO. Similarly, hydrogen and chlorine each have a valency of one and the formula of the compound formed between them must be HCl.

So far then we have—

$$ZnO + HCl \rightarrow$$

Now we must consider the products that are formed in the reaction. Analysis would show them to be zinc chloride $ZnCl_2$ (zinc valency 2 and chlorine valency 1) and water H_2O (hydrogen valency 1 and oxygen valency 2). We can now add a right-hand side to our equation.

$$ZnO + HCl \rightarrow ZnCl_2 + H_2O$$

The Law of Conservation of Mass states that in a chemical reaction matter is neither created nor destroyed. It follows that equal numbers of a particular type of atom must appear on either side of an equation. In our equation two atoms of both hydrogen and chlorine appear on the right-hand side but only one atom of each appears on the left. The equation can be balanced by replacing the one molecule of hydrogen chloride on the left-hand side with two molecules. In a balanced equation the arrow may be replaced by an equals sign.

$$ZnO + 2HCl = ZnCl_2 + H_2O$$

Summarizing, the steps in writing a chemical equation are—

1. Write down the formulae of the reacting chemicals.
2. Write in the formulae of the substances produced.
3. Balance the equation.
4. Check the equation.

Try writing a balanced equation for the reaction in which aluminium Al reacts with oxygen O_2 to form aluminium oxide Al_2O_3.

The Meaning of an Equation. Apart from providing a useful shorthand method of describing what happens in a chemical reaction, a balanced equation also tells us the weights of the reacting substances and of the products formed. We have already worked out a balanced equation for the reaction between zinc chloride and hydrochloric acid.

$$ZnO + 2HCl = ZnCl_2 + H_2O$$

Put into words, our balanced equation means that—
One molecule of zinc oxide reacts with two molecules of hydrochloric acid to form one molecule of zinc chloride and one molecule of water.

The molecular weights of the compounds involved can be obtained by adding the atomic weights of the particular atoms which they contain.

Atomic weights

$$Zn = 65, O = 16, H = 1, Cl = 35·5$$

Molecular weights

$$ZnO = 65 + 16 = 81$$

$$HCl = 1 + 35·5 = 36·5$$

$$ZnCl_2 = 65 + (35·5 \times 2) = 65 + 71 = 136$$

$$H_2O = (2 \times 1) + 16 = 2 + 16 = 18$$

Since molecular weights are the relative weights of molecules it follows that—
81 *parts by weight of* ZnO *reacts with* $2 \times 36·5$ *parts of* HCl *to form* 136 *parts of* $ZnCl_2$ *and* 18 *parts of water.*

We can select any units of weight but normally we would work in grammes and we can say that—
81 gm of ZnO react with 73 gm of HCl to form 136 gm of $ZnCl_2$ and 18 gm of water.

Worked Example. Calculate the weight of silver nitrate required to produce 70 gm of silver chloride using an excess of sodium chloride.

Silver chloride can be produced from silver nitrate in the following reaction—

Silver nitrate + Sodium chloride
                    = Silver chloride + Sodium nitrate

The balanced equation for this reaction is—

$$AgNO_3 + NaCl = AgCl + NaNO_3$$

Atomic Weights

Ag = 108, N = 14, Cl = 35·5, O = 16, Na = 23

Molecular Weights

$AgNO_3$ = 108 + 14 + (3 × 16) = 108 + 14 + 48 = 170

$NaCl$ = 23 + 35·5 = 58·5

$AgCl$ = 108 + 35·5 = 143·5

$NaNO_3$ = 23 + 14 + (3 × 16) = 23 + 14 + 48 = 85

From the equation—

1 molecule of $AgNO_3$ + 1 molecule of NaCl
          = 1 molecule of AgCl + 1 molecule of $NaNO_3$

170 gm of $AgNO_3$ + 58·5 gm of NaCl
          = 143·5 gm of AgCl + 85 gm of $NaNO_3$

143·5 gm of silver chloride AgCl can be produced from 170 gm of silver nitrate $AgNO_3$.

1 gm of silver chloride AgCl can be produced from $\dfrac{170}{143\cdot5}$ gm of silver nitrate $AgNO_3$.

70 gm of silver chloride AgCl can be produced from $\dfrac{143\cdot5}{170} \times 70$ gm of silver nitrate $AgNO_3$ = 82·9 gm of silver nitrate.

In this way it is possible to work out exactly the quantities of two chemicals which will react together and the quantities of the substances which are produced. On an industrial scale this type of calculation is of the greatest importance in planning efficient production.

TYPES OF CHEMICAL REACTION

All common chemical reactions, including those which are made use of in printing processes, fall into a number of distinct classes. These are—

1. Combination.
2. Decomposition.
3. Replacement.
4. Double decomposition (i.e. Double replacement).
5. Oxidation and Reduction.

1. Combination. In this type of reaction two or more substances join together to form one other substance.

$$A + B \rightarrow C$$

Examples

(a) If you heat a mixture of iron filings and powdered sulphur they combine to form iron sulphide

$$Fe + S = FeS$$

(b) A zinc plate combines with the oxygen in the air to form a layer of zinc oxide on its surface

$$2Zn + O_2 = 2ZnO$$

(c) The nitric oxide NO gas which may be given off when nitric acid attacks zinc combines with oxygen from the air to form the brown gas nitrogen peroxide NO_2

$$2NO + O_2 = 2NO_2$$

2. Decomposition. Many chemical compounds break up into two or more parts when they are heated

$$A \rightarrow B + C$$

Examples

(a) All carbonates with the exception of those of sodium and potassium decompose on heating into their oxides and carbon dioxide gas, e.g. Calcium carbonate $CaCO_3$

$$CaCO_3 = CaO + CO_2$$

(b) When potassium chlorate is heated oxygen is given off leaving potassium chloride

$$2KClO_3 = 2KCl + 3O_2$$

This is a useful method of making oxygen in a laboratory. It is an interesting reaction since the addition of a small quantity of manganese dioxide, a black powder, greatly increases the amount of oxygen given off. A substance which is able to assist a reaction in this way without actually changing chemically itself, is known as a *catalyst*

EXPERIMENT 1. PREPARATION OF OXYGEN

Apparatus. Boiling tube; glass tubing; gas jar; trough; Bunsen burner; bee-hive shelf.

Mix a small quantity of manganese dioxide with some potassium chlorate, add to the boiling tube and assemble the apparatus as shown in Fig. 10.1.

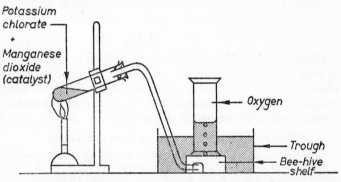

FIG. 10.1. APPARATUS FOR THE PREPARATION OF OXYGEN

Heat the boiling tube and collect the gas given off over water. A glowing splint will burst into flame in an atmosphere of oxygen.

3. Replacement. In this type of reaction one element replaces another in a compound.

$$AB + C \rightarrow AC + B$$

Examples

(a) If you dip the clean blade of a knife into a solution of copper sulphate a very thin layer of copper is deposited on to the steel blade containing iron, Fe

$$CuSO_4 + Fe = FeSO_4 + Cu$$

This copper is only loosely attached. If a thicker coating

properly bonded to the surface is required this must be electro-deposited (*see* page 244). Steel inking rollers and the image areas on an aluminium litho plate can be made temporarily more receptive to ink by treating them with a solution containing a copper salt.

(*b*) Acids and Metals (*see also* Chapter 15). All acids contain hydrogen which can often be directly replaced by a metal. Sulphuric acid attacks zinc to release hydrogen and leave zinc sulphate in solution—

$$H_2SO_4 + Zn = ZnSO_4 + H_2$$

Similarly hydrochloric acid attacks magnesium to release hydrogen and leave magnesium chloride in solution—

$$2HCl + Mg = MgCl_2 + H_2$$

Hydrochloric acid and sulphuric acid attack most metals, in each case freeing hydrogen and accepting the metal in its place. On the other hand, although nitric acid reacts with magnesium to give hydrogen, with all other common metals the gases given off are oxides of nitrogen.

EXPERIMENT 2. PREPARATION OF FERROUS SULPHATE

Apparatus. 250 ml-beaker; Bunsen burner; tripod; gauze; filter funnel.
Method. Add iron filings gradually to about 100 ml of warm dilute sulphuric acid in a beaker until no more gas is given off. Finally, bring the solution to the boil and filter while still hot. Evaporate to smaller bulk. Green crystals of ferrous sulphate will form when the clear solution is allowed to cool.

$$H_2SO_4 + Fe = FeSO_4 + H_2$$

(*c*) When a very small piece of metallic sodium is placed on to water in a shallow dish, a violent reaction occurs, the heat of which will melt the sodium into a round bead. The sodium has released hydrogen from the water and sodium hydroxide is formed

$$2H_2O + 2Na = 2NaOH + H_2$$

Since sodium hydroxide (caustic soda) is a strong alkali the solution which remains will turn red litmus blue.

4. Double Decomposition (Double Replacement). In a double decomposition reaction two compounds exchange parts of their molecules to form two other compounds. When two couples on the dance floor exchange their partners a sort of double decomposition has taken place—

$$AB + CD \rightarrow AD + CB$$

SPECIAL CASES OF DOUBLE DECOMPOSITION

(a) *Acid + Base = Salt + Water (Neutralization)*

For example, if hydrochloric acid is added gradually to sodium hydroxide until the solution is neutral to litmus, sodium chloride (common salt) and water are the only products of the reaction—

$$HCl + NaOH = NaCl + H_2O$$

The water can be evaporated off to leave crystals of sodium chloride.

(b) *Preparation of an Insoluble Salt from Two Soluble Salts.*

For example, if a solution of potassium iodide is added to a solution of silver nitrate, the yellow insoluble salt silver iodide AgI is immediately thrown out of solution—

$$AgNO_3 + KI = AgI + KNO_3$$

Silver iodide is one of the light sensitive silver salts used in a photographic emulsion (Chapter 16).

EXPERIMENT 3. TO PREPARE LEAD IODIDE

Add a solution of potassium iodide to a solution of lead nitrate. A bright yellow precipitate of lead iodide is immediately formed—

$$2KI + PbNO_3 = 2KNO_3 + PbI_2$$

If the lead iodide is filtered off, dissolved in a large volume of hot water and then left to cool, the salt can be obtained in the form of yellow needles.

5. Oxidation and Reduction. Many oxidation and reduction reactions fall into classes which we have already considered, but it is important that we should deal with them separately.

The simplest type of oxidation is *the addition of oxygen to a substance.* If you hold a small piece of magnesium ribbon with tongs in a Bunsen flame it quickly burns with a brilliant white light leaving behind a white powder. The magnesium has been *oxidized* to magnesium oxide MgO.

$$2Mg + O_2 = 2MgO$$

Most metals are oxidized to some extent by the oxygen in the air, the reaction being speeded up if they are heated. However, the oxygen gained by a substance need not be taken from the air. There are a number of chemicals which readily give up oxygen and these we call *oxidizing agents*. Among the more important of these are nitric acid, concentrated sulphuric acid, potassium dichromate, hydrogen peroxide, and ozone.

Oxidation is the principal drying method for letterpress and lithographic inks. Oxygen from the air combines with the resin vehicle of the ink to convert it slowly from a semi-liquid on the press into a tough hard solid on the paper (Chapter 20).

Reduction is the opposite of oxidation and the simplest type of reduction, therefore, is *the removal of oxygen from a substance*. The iron oxide in a blast furnace is reduced to iron by carbon monoxide CO—

$$Fe_2O_3 + 3CO = 2Fe + 3CO_2$$

The extraction of a metal from its ore often includes a reduction process like this in which the metal is freed from combined oxygen.

Those chemicals which will readily accept oxygen are called *reducing agents* and these include carbon monoxide, hydrogen, sulphur dioxide, and hydrogen sulphide.

EXPERIMENT 4. TO REDUCE LEAD OXIDE

Heat a small quantity of lead oxide (litharge) on a charcoal block using a blow pipe. Small beads of metallic lead will appear—

$$2PbO + C = 2Pb + CO_2$$

If one substance in a reaction gains oxygen, i.e. is oxidized, then another substance must lose it, i.e. be reduced. So oxidation and reduction always take place together.

For example, in the refining of copper from its ores, copper oxide is reduced to metallic copper by carbon monoxide.

Simultaneously the carbon monoxide is oxidized to carbon dioxide.

$$\overset{\longrightarrow\text{reduced}\longrightarrow}{Cu_2O + CO = 2Cu + CO_2}\underset{\longrightarrow\text{oxidized}\longrightarrow}{}$$

More general definitions of oxidation and reduction bring in reactions which do not involve oxygen. *We can consider oxidation for an atom or ion as being the loss of electrons, and reduction as being the gain of electrons.* An oxidizing agent is then a substance which accepts electrons, and a reducing agent a substance which gives them up. A great deal more chemistry has to be studied before these ideas can be properly understood but it is important at this stage to remember that oxygen does not have to take part in every oxidation and reduction reaction.

Examples: 1. When copper is etched with ferric chloride $FeCl_3$ the final products of the reaction appear to be cupric chloride $CuCl_2$ and ferrous chloride $FeCl_2$

$$Cu + 2FeCl_3 = CuCl_2 + 2FeCl_2$$

Copper has changed from Cu to the cupric ion Cu^{++}. Remembering that electrons are negatively charged particles this represents an electron loss, i.e. *copper oxidized.* On the other hand iron has changed from Fe^{+++}, the ferric ion, to Fe^{++}, the ferrous ion. This is an electron gain and the ferric ion has been *reduced.*

2. The light-sensitive material on a photographic plate is a silver salt, usually silver bromide, $AgBr$. Silver bromide consists of a lattice of silver ions Ag^+ and bromide ions Br^-. Basically what takes place during exposure and development is a reduction reaction.

$$Ag^+ \xrightarrow{\text{gains one electron}} Ag$$
$$\text{REDUCTION}$$

present   Black
in silver   metallic
bromide   silver
lattice

The main ingredient in the developing bath is a reducing agent of exactly the right strength (e.g. hydroquinone), i.e. a supplier of electrons. Those silver bromide grains which have been struck by light will accept the electrons offered by the reducing agent to form a black silver image.

THINGS TO LEARN

1. The molecular weight is the weight of one molecule of a substance compared with the weight of one-sixteenth of an atom of oxygen. The molecular weight of a compound is obtained by adding the atomic weights of all of the atoms present in one molecule of that compound.

2. A chemical equation describes what happens in a chemical reaction and indicates the weights of the substance which will react together and of the products formed.

3. All common chemical reactions fall into a number of distinct classes.

Combination	$A + B \rightarrow C$
Decomposition	$A \rightarrow B + C$
Replacement	$AB + C \rightarrow AC + B$
Double decomposition	$AB + CD \rightarrow AD + CB$

4. A catalyst is a substance which will change the speed of a reaction but is itself unchanged at the end of the reaction.

OTHER BOOKS TO READ

See Chapter 3.

EXERCISES

1. $2Mg + O_2 = 2MgO$.
Explain fully the meaning of this equation. What weight of MgO would you expect to remain when 18 gm of Mg has been burnt in air? (Atomic weights, Mg = 24, O = 16.)

2. Magnesium is attacked by nitric acid HNO_3 to give magnesium nitrate $Mg(NO_3)_2$ and hydrogen gas H_2. Work out a balanced equation for this reaction and use it to work out the theoretical weight of nitric acid required to dissolve 4 oz of magnesium (atomic weights, Mg = 24, N = 14, O = 16).

3. Give the full meaning of the following equation in words.

$$NaOH + HCl = NaCl + H_2O$$

(Atomic weights, Na = 23, O = 16, H = 1, Cl = 35·5)

(Photo/1961/Int.)

4. What is the percentage by weight of oxygen in zinc oxide ZnO and in zinc sulphate $ZnSO_4$? (Atomic weights, Zn = 65, O = 16, S = 32.)

5. (a) Describe the chemical reaction which takes place when zinc is etched by sulphuric acid. Express the reaction in the form of a chemical equation. (b) Explain the meaning of a chemical equation and show how it can be used to calculate the weight of the ingredients required for a chemical reaction. As an example, calculate the theoretical weight of sulphuric acid required to dissolve 7 lb of zinc (atomic weights Zn = 65, S = 32, O = 16). (E and S/1960/Fin.)

6. What is the theoretical weight of anhydrous copper sulphate obtainable from the treatment of 1,000 lb of copper with sulphuric acid? (Atomic weights, Cu = 64, S = 32, O = 16.) (E and S/1959/Fin.)

7. Explain what is meant by: (a) a replacement reaction; and (b) a double decomposition reaction and give one example of each.

8. Define oxidation and reduction. Give three examples of oxidation reactions in printing processes.

pH AND PRINTING

MANY people think that the English delicacy, fish and chips, is improved by vinegar, which is about 5 per cent acetic acid. It is most unlikely that anyone would want to replace the vinegar with 5 per cent sulphuric acid. If they did, their meal would probably blacken and start to disappear. They might even find that their knife and fork had become smaller.

Both solutions are acids and so they would each turn litmus red, taste sour, and neutralize a base to form a salt. Yet, though they are both 5 per cent solutions, the sulphuric acid has much stronger acid properties than the acetic, e.g. it attacks metals more readily and, of course, fish and chips.

If you add a small piece of granulated zinc to each of two test tubes, one containing a 1 per cent solution of acetic acid and the other a 1 per cent solution of sulphuric acid, the sulphuric will cause the more vigorous reaction. Differences in acidity and alkalinity of this type can be measured on the pH scale. In this chapter we shall discuss the meaning of pH, how it can be measured and why it has become important to the printer.

Basic Ideas of pH. pH is a measure of the relative acidity or alkalinity of solutions in water. It is a measurable property of a solution in much the same way as temperature. Just as we give the temperature of a solution a number on a scale of temperature like the centigrade scale, so we give the pH of a solution a number on the pH scale.

The most useful part of the pH scale runs from 0 to 14. A neutral solution has a pH of 7. Acidic solutions have a pH of less than 7, the more strongly acid the nearer to zero. Similarly, alkaline solutions have a pH greater than 7, the more strongly alkaline the nearer to 14. Fig. 11.1 shows the pH of a number of common solutions.

Each point on the scale represents a definite degree of

acidity or alkalinity. The scale is so arranged that every time the acidity or alkalinity changes by a factor of 10 the pH changes by 1·0 pH units. For example, a solution of pH 6 has only one-tenth the acidity of a solution with pH 5. A solution of pH 2 is 100 times as acidic as a solution of pH 4.

A Background to pH. If we connect the positive terminal of a battery to a piece of copper and the negative terminal to

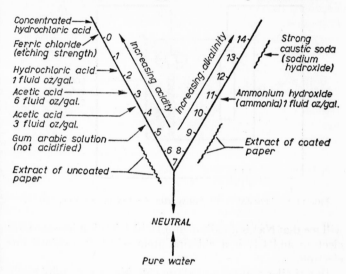

FIG. 11.1. pH SCALE OF SOME COMMON SOLUTIONS

a key, immersed separately in a solution of copper sulphate, a thin coating of copper is deposited on to the key (Fig. 11.2).

The passage of a current of electricity has caused a chemical change to take place.

Copper sulphate is an *electrolyte, a substance which when molten or when dissolved in water will conduct an electric current.* This large class of substances includes most acids, bases, and salts. When an electrolyte dissolves in water, it breaks down into charged atoms or groups of atoms called *ions.* For example, sodium chloride (common salt) NaCl breaks down into positively charged sodium ions Na$^+$ and negatively charged chlorine ions Cl$^-$ according to the equation—

$$NaCl \rightarrow Na^+ + Cl^-$$

This process in which a substance divides into charged parts is known as *ionization.* If you refer back to page 33 on which the atomic structures of both sodium and chlorine are given, you

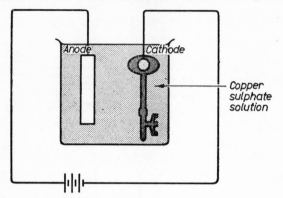

FIG. 11.2. APPARATUS TO SHOW THE ACTION OF AN ELECTROLYTE

will see that Na$^+$ is a sodium atom which has lost its outermost electron and Cl$^-$ is a chlorine atom which has gained one electron.

In a similar manner to sodium chloride, copper sulphate in solution breaks down into two "halves," one positively charged (copper ion Cu^{++}) and the other negatively charged (sulphate ion SO$_4^{--}$).

$$CuSO_4 \rightarrow Cu^{++} + SO_4^{--}$$

It is these ions which are able to act as the carriers of electric current. In our example of copper plating the Cu^{++} ions are attracted to the negative terminal (the cathode) where a supply of electrons (electric current) is waiting to convert them into Cu, metallic copper.

Strong and Weak Acids. We have already mentioned that most acids are electrolytes. All of them contain hydrogen in their molecules. When acids are dissolved or diluted in water a certain percentage of their molecules split into two parts, hydrogen now positively charged and the rest of the molecule negatively charged. For example, hydrochloric acid HCl and nitric acid HNO_3 dissociate in the following way—

$$HCl \rightarrow H^+ + Cl^-$$

$$HNO_3 \rightarrow H^+ + NO_3^-$$

It is now recognized that acid properties such as their sour

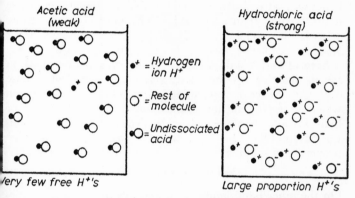

FIG. 11.3. THE HYDROGEN ION CONTENT OF ACIDS

taste and their corrosive effects are due to the presence of H^+ or hydrogen ions as they are called. The more H^+ ions there are in a certain volume of solution, the more acidic will be the properties of that solution. We have already seen that a certain percentage of the total number of acid molecules break down into ions. This percentage varies with different acids. For example, well over 90 per cent of the molecules of hydrochloric acid dissociate into ions. This means that its solutions contain high concentrations of hydrogen ions and hence show strongly acidic properties. On the other hand less than 1 per cent of acetic acid molecules dissociate in water. Therefore acetic acid solutions will always have quite low concentrations of hydrogen ions and will only show weakly acidic properties (Fig. 11.3).

Because different acids dissociate to different extents it will be seen that a knowledge of the actual weight of acid per unit volume does not give information on the acidity of a solution. What we need to know is the number of hydrogen ions in a solution and pH is a measure of hydrogen ion concentration: the more hydrogen ions, the more acidic the solution and the lower the number on the pH scale. It will now be clearer why in Fig. 11.1 we read that 1 fluid oz/gal hydrochloric acid is more acidic (i.e. has a lower pH) than 6 fluid oz/gal acetic acid. It is simply that hydrochloric acid is able to supply many more hydrogen ions than acetic acid. The most common strong acids are hydrochloric, sulphuric and nitric whilst the weak acids include acetic, tartaric, oxalic, carbonic, and boric.

Strong and Weak Alkalis. A similar situation exists on the alkaline side. Sodium hydroxide is a strong alkali because of its high degree of dissociation into ions. In this case the ion which is responsible for alkaline properties is the OH^- or hydroxyl ion. Sodium hydroxide gives rise to large concentrations of OH^- ions and therefore has strongly alkaline properties in solution.

$$NaOH \rightarrow Na^+ + OH^-$$

On the other hand ammonia dissociates much less, provides fewer hydroxyl ions and is less alkaline

$$NH_4OH \rightarrow NH_4^+ + OH^-$$

As the concentration of hydroxyl ions in a solution increases the concentration of hydrogen ions decreases proportionally. This is the reason why the one scale of pH measuring hydrogen ion concentration can be used to assess solutions on both the acid and the alkaline side of neutral. Thus a solution of sodium hydroxide, with more hydroxyl ions than a solution of ammonia, has fewer hydrogen ions and therefore a numerically higher pH. When the number of H^+ ions in a solution exactly equals the number of OH^- ions then that solution is neutral and has a pH of 7.

The Effects of pH. The effects of varying pH are to be found in many processes within the printing industry. Some of the more important of these will now be discussed individually.

Paper and Retarded Drying. Apart from the various fibres which go into making a sheet of paper, many chemicals also play their part. The result is that the final paper may be acid, alkaline or neutral and it has a pH which can be measured by extraction. The pH of an uncoated paper or board will normally be between 5 and 7. The pH of the surface of a coated paper is usually higher and may be between 8 and 10. In recent years a good deal of evidence has been found to show that the pH of a paper is one of the factors influencing the drying of a letterpress or a lithographic ink. The drying time increases as the pH of the paper surface decreases, if other factors are constant, and at low pH's, i.e. below 5, the drying may be seriously retarded or even stopped altogether. Another factor influencing the drying time of this type of ink is the relative humidity of the atmosphere. The higher the relative humidity the slower is the rate of drying. Evidence suggests that low pH has its greatest effect on the drying of an ink when the relative humidity is also high. Both PATRA and the Lithographic Technical Foundation have worked on this problem. The results of one experiment carried

Table 6

THE INFLUENCE OF RELATIVE HUMIDITY AND THE pH OF PAPER ON THE DRYING OF LETTERPRESS PRINTS (PATRA)

Paper pH	Drying Time of Prints (hours)	
	at 65%	at 75%
6·9	6·6	14
5·5	6·7	23
5·4	7.0	30
4·9	7·3	38
4·7	7·6	60
4·4	7·6	80

out at PATRA are shown in Table 6 and Fig. 11.4. Since relative humidities are generally higher in litho than in letter-press, pH control is all the more vital in that process.

The Fountain Solution in Lithography. In litho it is common practice to add chemicals to the water in the fountain. There are good reasons for these additions when gum arabic or cellulose gum are being used to desensitize the non-image areas. The efficiency of these desensitizers is increased as you add acid to the solution, i.e. lower the pH, but a point is soon

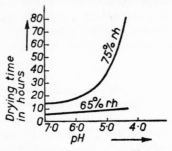

FIG. 11.4. THE INFLUENCE OF RELATIVE HUMIDITY AND THE pH OF PAPER ON THE DRYING OF LETTERPRESS PRINTS (PATRA)

reached when the addition of more acid will seriously retard the drying of the ink and eventually at low pH's the plate will be attacked. With aluminium there is less risk of plate attack than there is with zinc. If on the other hand the pH of the fountain solution moved above the neutral point and it became alkaline the gum would lose its desensitizing properties, and the non-image areas would become greasy and start to print. It will be seen how important it is for the lithographer to control the pH of his fountain solution.

Dichromated Colloids. The production of printing plates usually involves the exposure to light through a negative or positive of a coating of a dichromated colloid on the metal (Chapter 17). The coating is hardened and made less soluble in water in proportion to the amount of light falling on a particular point. The plate can then be developed and the metal selectively etched through the resist.

The sensitivity of the coating to light depends on a number of factors including the pH. In fact the higher the pH of the coating the lower is its sensitivity, so the photo-process worker as well as the printer can suffer from the effects of varying pH.

There are other examples of processes within the industry where pH control is needed. The pH of a paper or an adhesive may cause a particular ink to change colour and the tarnishing of bronze powder by sulphides is much more likely to take place at low pH's. In general one can say that wherever an aqueous solution plays a part in a process, pH may be an influencing factor.

The Measurement of pH. The methods of measuring pH can be divided into two broad classes—

1. Methods using indicators.
2. Electrical methods.

1. *Indicators* are coloured substances, soluble in water, which change colour when the pH of the solution in which they are dissolved is changed. The colour change is reversible and it is caused by a change in the chemical structure of the molecules of indicator. Any one indicator only changes colour over quite a small part of the pH scale; normally this portion covers between 1·5 and 2·0 pH units. For example, the indicator methyl red is coloured red in a solution of pH 4·2 and yellow in a solution of pH 6·3. Between these points the colour change is gradual but on either side of them there is no colour change at all (Fig. 11.5).

EXPERIMENT 1. THE BEHAVIOUR OF AN INDICATOR

Add a small amount of dilute ammonia to about 50 c.c. of water in a small conical flask. This solution is now alkaline with a pH greater than 7. Add a few drops of methyl red, colouring the solution yellow. A 1 per cent solution of acetic acid should now be added a drop at a time, shaking the flask between each addition and noting the colour. The mixed solution will remain yellow until pH 6·3 is reached. Below that the colour will slowly pass through orange to red at pH 4·2. Any further additions of acetic acid will not affect the colour.

It follows that a single indicator is useful only over a part of the pH range. Since there are many indicators, each with its own particular range, a series of them can be selected to cover almost all of the pH scale. In addition, it has been possible to devise a standard mixture of indicators in definite proportions which shows a gradual colour change over the whole range. These universal indicators, as they are called, normally change from red at pH 3·0 through various shades

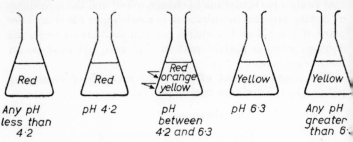

Fig. 11.5. Solutions Containing Methyl Red Indicator

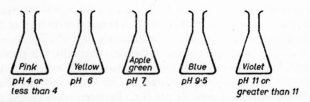

Fig. 11.6. Solutions Containing B.D.H. Universal Indicator

of orange, yellow, green, blue, and violet to red-violet at pH 11·0, each colour corresponding to a definite pH (Fig. 11.6).

EXPERIMENTAL

Add a few drops of a universal indicator to about 50 c.c. of dilute ammonia solution in a conical flask. Note the colour and then start making gradual additions of dilute acetic acid, shaking the flask between each addition. The colour changes slowly as the pH of the solution passes through the neutral point to pH 3.

A list is shown below of some of the indicators used for pH determination together with the range of pH over which they show a colour change.

Indicator	pH Range	Colour Change
bromo-phenol blue	2·8–4·6	yellow–blue
bromo-cresol green	3·6–5·2	yellow–blue
methyl red	4·2–6·3	red–yellow
bromo-thymol blue	6·0–7·6	yellow–blue
cresol red	7·2–8·8	yellow–red
thymol blue	8·0–9·6	yellow–blue

Each of the indicator methods of measuring pH depends upon the assumption that, if a particular indicator in two different solutions has the same colour, then the solutions have the same pH. In practice this may not always be completely true.

INDICATOR METHODS

(a) **The B.D.H. Comparator.** In order to measure pH with indicators one has to refer to standard solutions of accurately known pH. These solutions are known as "buffer solutions." For convenience they may be supplied in sealed hard glass tubes each one containing a solution of known pH and a definite amount of a particular indicator. There may be 9 or 10 tubes for each indicator produced in steps of 0·2 units of pH. The solution under test is put in a tube of the same type together with the correct amount of the appropriate indicator, and the buffer tube whose colour comes nearest to the colour of this test solution is found by comparison. If, for example, the colour appears to be midway between the 3·8 and the 4·0 tubes, then it is reasonable to take 3·9 as the approximate pH of the solution.

The B.D.H. small block comparator, shown in Fig. 11.7 (a), is a plastic device which will carry the tubes separated by black partitions. The three central pairs of compartments are linked and provided with windows, through which the colours of the tubes can be viewed against the light. If the six central compartments are used in the way shown in Fig. 11.7 (b) any slight colour or cloudiness in the test solution is taken into account.

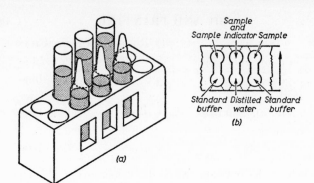

FIG. 11.7 (a). THE B.D.H. SMALL BLOCK COMPARATOR
(b) Arrangement of tubes in six central compartments

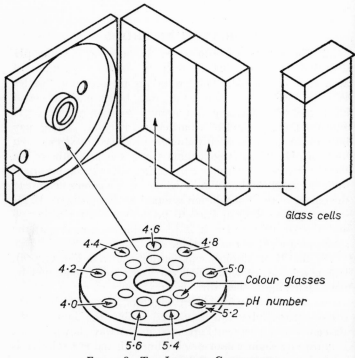

Glass cells

4·6
4·4   4·8
4·2   5·0
4·0   Colour glasses
                pH number
          5·2
    5·6 5·4

FIG. 11.8 THE LOVIBOND COMPARATOR

EXPERIMENT 2. pH MEASUREMENT (1)

Use a B.D.H. comparator to find the pH of—

(a) tap water;
(b) distilled water.

(b) **The Lovibond Comparator.** In this instrument the pH of a solution is determined by comparing the colour of the test solution plus indicator with permanent colour glasses. These glasses have been developed to match exactly buffer solutions containing a given quantity of indicator. The comparator, shown in Fig. 11.8, consists of a bakelite case opening like a book which is furnished at the back with an opal glass screen and two compartments to take tubes of square cross-section containing the liquid under examination.

In the front portion are two round holes situated side by side opposite to the glass screen and coinciding with the partitions for the tubes. The standard coloured glasses, nine in number, are fitted into a flat bakelite disc which may be rotated in front of the case. This brings each of the standard colours in turn opposite the left-hand hole behind which is a tube filled with the liquid being tested. The right-hand glass tube contains 10 ml of the same liquid to which 0·5 ml of the appropriate indicator has been added. This coloured solution is viewed through the right-hand hole and compared with the permanent colour standards on the left-hand side.

In this way compensation is made for any inherent colour of the liquid. The pH value corresponding with the colour in view is indicated by the figures on the ivorine disc which appears in a third hole in front of the case.

Each bakelite disc containing the standard colour glasses represents the complete colour change of one indicator in steps of 0·2 pH. In addition there is a disc designed for use with the universal indicator with larger steps.

EXPERIMENT 3. pH MEASUREMENT (2)

Use a Lovibond comparator to find the pH of—

(a) A 0·1 per cent solution of acetic acid;
(b) A 0·1 per cent solution of hydrochloric acid.

(c) **Indicator Papers.** Litmus paper provided one of the earliest means of distinguishing acid from alkaline solutions and test papers prepared with indicators like bromo-cresol green, thymol blue, etc., give us the simplest of all the methods of measuring pH. Unfortunately, they are not suitable for use with all types of solutions and so they are of restricted application. However, for certain types of pH control they do provide a very quick and convenient method of checking the approximate pH of a solution.

Indicator papers prepared from special mixed indicators such as the B.D.H. "Wide-range" and "Narrow-range" papers are a later refinement. As with the use of B.D.H. universal indicators in the comparator methods so the "Wide-range" papers can be used to show which "Narrow-range" papers to select. The papers available from B.D.H. are as follows—

				Range
B.D.H. Narrow-range Indicator papers				2·5–4·0
,,	,,	,,	,,	4·0–5·5
,,	,,	,,	,,	5·5–7·0
,,	,,	,,	,,	7·0–8·5
,,	,,	,,	,,	8·5–10·0
B.D.H. Wide-range Indicator papers				2·0–10·5

The important advantages of the indicator methods of measuring pH are speed, simplicity, and cheapness. The accuracy given by an instrument like the Lovibond Comparator would be quite adequate for most of the possible uses in the printing industry. However, these methods do have drawbacks under certain conditions. If the solutions are coloured to any great extent the tests are more difficult to judge.

Electrical Methods. A more accurate but more expensive method of measuring pH is with a pH meter. There are several types of these meters varying in accuracy and price.

In a pH meter the solution to be measured is made part of a primary cell. Any cell produces a voltage which depends partly on the chemicals which are in the solution connecting the electrodes of the cell. A cell for the measurement of pH is arranged so that the voltage developed changes with the concentration of hydrogen ions in this solution.

The advantages of electrical methods are that great accuracy can be obtained when care is exercised and that they can be designed to give continuous readings. However, the instruments do need continual checking, they are more expensive

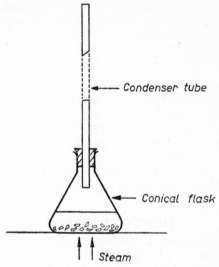

Condenser tube

Conical flask

Steam

FIG. 11.9. THE AQUEOUS EXTRACTION OF PAPER

than any colour comparator and they require skilled handling to give really accurate results. The choice between electrical and indicator methods obviously depends on circumstances.

Measuring the pH of Paper. In order to measure reliably the pH of a paper it is necessary to extract the acidic or alkalinic materials from the paper with water, and then to test the extract. Standard methods of hot and cold extraction have been laid down by the Technical Association of the Pulp and Paper Industry (TAPPI). PATRA now recommend the hot extraction method which is basically as outlined in the following experiment. B.S. 2924, dealing with the pH of paper, contains the details of the method.

Using the hot extraction method and a pH meter or a Lovibond comparator measure the pH of—

(a) Any uncoated paper;
(b) The surface of any coated paper (*see* p. 262 for method of carrying out this experiment).

Weigh out 1 gm of the paper and add to 70 ml of distilled water in a small conical flask fitted with a reflux condenser (Fig. 11.9). Heat on a water bath for 1 hour, keeping the temperature of the extract near to 96°C. Cool, pour off the liquid and measure its pH using a pH meter or a Lovibond comparator in the usual way.

Some printing laboratories make a rapid check of the pH of a new consignment of paper by smearing an indicator straight on the paper surface and observing the colour change. The method is not particularly reliable. The Lovibond–PATRA colour slides are claimed to improve this method whilst retaining its speed and simplicity. The slides consist of three sets of nine standard glasses which match the commonly used indicators when employed to stain paper.

THINGS TO LEARN

1. pH is a measure of the relative acidity or alkalinity of aqueous solutions. The main part of the pH scale runs from 0 to 14. A neutral solution has a pH of 7. Acid solutions have a pH of less than 7, the more strongly acid the nearer to zero. Similarly alkaline solutions have a pH greater than 7, the more strongly alkaline the nearer to 14.

2. The pH of a solution may be measured by—

(a) Methods using indicators, e.g. Colour comparators, Indicator papers.

(b) Electrical methods, i.e. pH meters.

OTHER BOOKS TO READ

R. B. WEBBER, *The Book of pH* (George Newnes)

P. J. HARTSUCH, *Chemistry of Lithography* (Lithographic Technical Foundation, New York)

Proceedings of PATRA Conferences

EXERCISES

1. Describe the difference between atoms and ions, illustrating your answer with reference to aqueous solutions of copper sulphate, sodium chloride, sodium hydroxide, sulphuric acid, and hydrochloric acid.
(Photo/1956/Fin.)

2. What is meant by the chemical terms "strong acid," "weak acid," "strong base," and "weak base"? Give two examples of each type of acid and base and say how they are used in the graphic arts.
(Photo/1961/Fin.)

3. What is meant by the measurement of pH? Why is it important for the printer to know the pH value of certain of the materials he uses?
(Lp Mc 1959/Fin.)

4. Explain as completely as possible the meaning of "hydrogen ion concentration," illustrating the answer by reference to the changes in pH which take place when potassium hydroxide is titrated with a "strong acid" solution.
(Photo/1954/Fin.)

5. Explain why a 1 per cent solution of hydrochloric acid has a lower pH than a 1 per cent solution of acetic acid.

6. Describe fully the pH scale, methods of measuring on it and its application in lithography.
(Litho/1961/Fin.)

7. Place in order on the pH scale 5 per cent solutions of acetic acid, sodium hydroxide, sodium chloride, and nitric acid.

Give your reasons for putting them in this particular order.

8. (a) What is the chemical definition of an acid? (b) What chemical properties do you determine when you carry out a pH measurement on a plating solution?
(E and S/1959/Int.)

9. The pH of a certain paper is said to be 4·0.

(a) Explain the meaning of this figure.

(b) How would you confirm it?

(c) What is the practical significance of this figure for the use of the paper?
(FTC/1961.)

CHAPTER 12

LIGHT

Heat and Light are Both Forms of Radiation. If you switch on an electric fire in a darkened room, current flowing through the element of the fire raises its temperature and heat rays are given off which the skin is able to detect and report to the brain. A few seconds later the eye will detect light rays

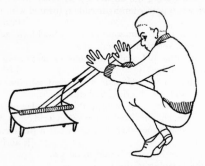

FIG. 12.1. HEAT AND LIGHT ARE BOTH FORMS OF RADIATION

given off as the element glows, first a dull red and then bright red (Fig. 12.1).

Though we can "feel heat" and "see light" there are many other forms of radiation, including ultra-violet, radio, television, gamma, and X-rays. This whole family of rays we call *electromagnetic radiations*. All of these travel at the same speed in any particular medium. In air this speed is about 186,000 miles per second, but in water it is reduced to about three-quarters of this and in glass to two-thirds. These forms of radiation, including light and heat, travel in the form of waves, vibrating at right angles to their direction of travel. Fig. 12.2 shows a ray vibrating in one plane only—the plane of the paper. This is a simplification, since light rays should be considered as vibrating in all planes at right angles to the direction of travel simultaneously.

The distance from a point on one wave to the corresponding point on the next is called the wavelength. This is shown in the diagram. The various waves we have mentioned including light, heat (infra red), ultra-violet, etc., differ only in their wavelength. The length of a wave may vary from 10,000

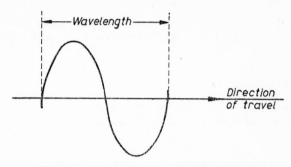

FIG. 12.2. RADIATION TRAVELLING IN WAVES

metres (about 6 miles) for a radio wave down to $\frac{1}{1000}$ of a millimicron for a gamma wave.

Note

$$1 \text{ millimetre (mm)} = \frac{1}{1,000} \text{ metre (m)}$$

$$1 \text{ micron } (\mu) = \frac{1}{1,000} \text{ mm} = \frac{1}{1,000,000} \text{ m}$$

$$1 \text{ millimicron } (m\mu) = \frac{1}{1,000} \mu = \frac{1}{1,000,000} \text{ mm}$$

$$= \frac{1}{1,000,000,000} \text{ m}$$

In talking about the wavelength of light we shall be using the very small mμ (pronounced milli-mu). In pure physics another unit is in common use, the ångström,

$$1 \text{ ångström (Å)} = \frac{1}{10{,}000} \mu = \frac{1}{10{,}000{,}000} \text{ mm}$$

$$= \frac{1}{10{,}000{,}000{,}000} \text{ m}$$

$$1 \text{ m}\mu = 10 \text{ Å}.$$

From the enormous range of electromagnetic waves shown in Fig. 12.3 the eye is only able to detect a very small portion,

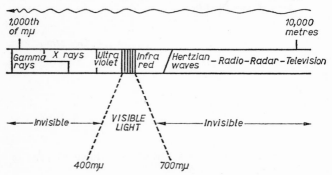

FIG. 12.3. ELECTROMAGNETIC WAVES

those with wavelengths between approximately 400 mμ and 700 mμ.

If all these wavelengths between 400 mμ and 700 mμ gave the same response to our eyes we should live in a black and white world or even a black and blue one. Fortunately, the different wavelengths in the range appear as different colours to our eyes. Light with a wavelength of 400 mμ gives a violet response, wavelengths at about 700 mμ appear red and in the middle of the visible spectrum around 550 mμ they appear green. If the whole range from 400 mμ to 700 mμ arrives together then we get the sensation of white light.

In the field of radio and television waves it is more usual to give the *frequency* of the waves rather than the wavelength.

The frequency is the number of complete waves which pass a given point in a second. For example, the BBC light programme is transmitted at a wavelength of 1,500 metres or a frequency of 200,000 waves per second. If you multiply the length of a wave by the number of waves passing per second you get the velocity of the electromagnetic wave. Using our example—

$$\text{Velocity} = 1,500 \times 200,000 \text{ metres per second}$$
$$= 300,000,000 \text{ metres per second}$$

(or about 186,000 miles per second).

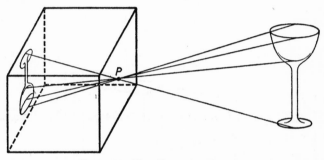

FIG. 12.4. THE PIN-HOLE CAMERA

What is the frequency of violet light with a wavelength of 400 mμ?*

Light Travels in Straight Lines. Our everyday experience, whether it be the sharp shadows cast by strong sunlight, the straight beam of a car's headlamps or the sometimes unfortunate fact that we cannot see round corners, tells us that light travels in straight lines. The pin-hole camera is another simple demonstration of this. A small pin-hole P is made in one end of a totally enclosed box and a ground-glass plate put in place of the side opposite the hole. If you look at the glass screen when the camera is pointing at a well illuminated object, e.g. a window, you will see an inverted image of this object. Fig. 12.4 shows how this image is formed.

* The answer is 750,000,000,000 000 wave per second.

A really sharp image can only be obtained when the pin-hole is small.

We call the path taken by light as represented by a line, a *ray* of light. A collection of rays is called a *beam*, which may be *parallel, converging,* or *diverging* (Fig. 12.5).

FIG. 12.5. BEAMS OF LIGHT

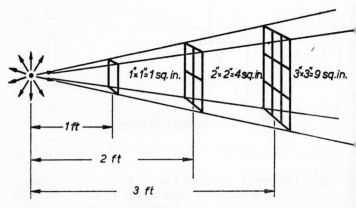

FIG. 12.6. THE INVERSE SQUARE LAW

The Inverse Square Law. If we consider a point source of light, it is clear that rays of light must travel out in straight lines from the source in all directions (Fig. 12.6). If we hold a piece of card one inch square one foot away from the source a small proportion of the light will fall on the card giving it a certain "intensity of illumination." At any distance greater than one foot the light which falls on the card will be spread over a greater area and the intensity of illumination on anything put in its path will be proportionately less. Two feet away from the source it would cover a card two inches square (area = 4 sq. in.) and three feet away it would cover a card three inches square (area = 9 sq. in.) (Fig. 12.6). Since the area covered at B is four times that at A, it follows that the intensity of illumination on a card placed at B is $\frac{1}{4}$ of that on a card placed at A. Similarly, the intensity at C is $\frac{4}{9}$ that at B. This relationship gives us the Inverse Square Law of light which states that *the intensity of illumination E over a surface due to a point source of light decreases as the square of the distance d from the lamp*, or

$$E \propto \frac{1}{d^2}.$$

The inverse square law is important to the photo-process worker since the position of the light source influences the exposure of a photographic emulsion in a camera and the exposure of a layer of dichromated colloid when printing down an image on to metal. The light sources which we use are never points, but they are usually small enough to be considered as such, e.g. a printing-down exposure is eight minutes with the lamp placed four feet from the frame. What exposure would be necessary to give a similar result if the lamp was moved in one foot?

Intensity of illumination with the lamp at 3 ft = $(\frac{4}{3})^2 = \frac{16}{9}$ of that at 4 ft.

For the same amount of light the exposure must be $\frac{9}{16}$ as long = $\frac{9}{16} \times 8 = 4\frac{1}{2}$ min.

Absorption, Reflection, and Transmission. A sheet of glass or clear film will allow a large proportion of the light falling on it to pass through or be *transmitted*. A material through which you are able to see objects clearly, is called *transparent* (Fig. 12.7 (*a*)). A material like ground glass which lets light through but scatters it in doing so is called *translucent* (Fig. 12.7 (*b*)) whilst a substance like thick card, metal foil or black paper transmitting no light is *opaque* (Fig. 12.7 (*c*, *d*, and *e*)). Light which is not transmitted may either be *absorbed* or *reflected*.

Specular Reflection. For regular or *specular* reflection to occur the surface must be smooth; mirrors, polished metal

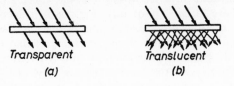

Transparent   Translucent
(a)   (b)

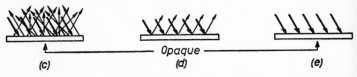

Opaque

(c)   (d)   (e)

Fig. 12.7. Absorption, Reflection, and Transmission

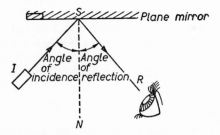

Fig. 12.8. Reflection at a Plane Mirror

surfaces, and glossy paper all meet this condition. A plane mirror usually consists of thin glass with a silvered back surface.

Experiment 1. Reflection at a Plane Mirror

Apparatus. Ray box: drawing board; plane mirror; drawing cartridge; drawing pins; pins; protractor.

Place a plane mirror on a sheet of white cartridge paper on a drawing board as shown in Fig. 12.8, marking its position. With the room darkened project a ray of light from the ray box on to the mirror. Draw a line *IS* along the path of this ray and mark in a point on the path of the reflected ray. Remove the mirror and ray box, complete the line *SR* and draw the normal at *S* (a line at right angles to the mirror at *S*). Measure the angle of incidence *ISN* and the angle of reflection *NSR* with a protractor. Repeat the experiment with a number of different angles of incidence.

In each case *the angle of incidence will equal the angle of reflection*. This is known as the first law of reflection. The second law states that *the incident ray and the reflected ray are always in the same plane*.

An image in a plane mirror has certain distinct properties. It is found as far behind the mirror as the object is in front, it is the same size as the object and it is a *virtual* image, i.e. it cannot be thrown on to a screen like the *real* image produced in a camera or by any type of projector. In addition it is laterally inverted, which means that the left-hand side of the image corresponds with the right-hand side of the object and vice versa (Fig. 12.9 (*a*)). If two mirrors are combined as in Fig. 12.9 (*b*) an image is obtained which is not laterally reversed. This is the principle used in the periscope. Fig. 12.9 (*c*) shows how three mirrors can be combined to give the straight line reversal sometimes required in a dark-room camera although to get an upright reversed image by this system the object must be placed on its side. Try constructing these systems using plane mirrors, retort stands, and clamps. In a process camera some of the mirrors may be replaced by reflecting prisms.

Diffuse Reflection. This paper reflects light but, since it has not got a smooth, highly polished surface, the light is not regularly reflected but is scattered in all directions (Fig. 12.7 (*c*)). We call this *diffuse* reflection. We are able to see most everyday objects by the light diffusely reflected from their surface.

Refraction. You will have noticed that a straight stick standing partly immersed in water appears to be bent at the surface and that a swimming pool appears to be shallower than it actually is. Both of these effects are due to refraction, which is the bending of light as it passes from one transparent substance into another, e.g. from air to glass or from water into air. This bending is due to a change in the speed of the light on entering the second medium.

Mirror
image

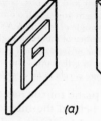

(a)

Straight line non-reversal

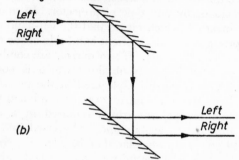

Left
Right

Left
Right

(b)

Straight line reversal

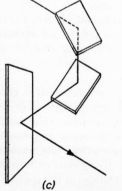

(c)

FIG. 12.9. ARRANGEMENTS OF PLANE MIRRORS

Fig. 12.10 shows what happens if you project a ray of light on to a glass surface. Most of the light enters the glass but is bent towards the normal. The angle i is called the angle of incidence and the angle r the angle of refraction. Notice that some of the light is specularly reflected from the surface.

If the experiment is repeated with water in place of the glass the ray entering the water is again bent towards the

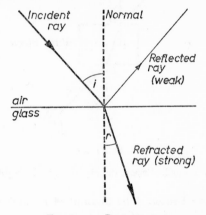

FIG. 12.10. REFRACTION

normal but by a smaller amount. In fact, when light passes from any transparent medium into another of greater density it is refracted *towards* the normal. When it passes from the dense to the less dense medium then it is refracted *away from* the normal.

EXPERIMENT 2. REFRACTION THROUGH A RECTANGULAR GLASS BLOCK

Apparatus. Drawing board; rectangular glass block; drawing cartridge; pins.

Place the glass block near the centre of the paper on a drawing board and mark its position as shown in Fig. 12.11. Remove the block and draw in a line AB to represent the path of a ray incident at B about halfway along the surface of the block. Place two pins P and Q evenly spaced on AB to mark the path of this ray. Now view these pins from the other side of the block and place two further pins R and S in a position where they appear in the same straight line as the images of P and Q. Remove the glass block, join the points *R* and *S* and extend the line to meet the block at *C*. *CS* now represents the path of the ray leaving the block. Join *BC*, draw in the normals at *B* and *C* and measure the angle of incidence *ABN* and the angle of refraction *CBL*. Notice that on leaving the glass the ray is bent

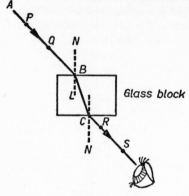

FIG. 12.11

away from the normal. Repeat the experiment with a different angle of incidence.

Refractive Index. The amount of refraction which will occur at the boundary of any two transparent media is given by the constant known as the refractive index which is equal to the ratio—

$$\frac{\text{Speed of light in the first medium}}{\text{Speed of light in the second medium}}$$

This ratio can be calculated from the relationship—

$$\text{Refractive index } \mu \text{ (pronounced mu)} = \frac{\sin i}{\sin r}$$

where *i* is the angle of incidence and *r* the angle of refraction. Thus if in an experiment $i = 30°$ and $r = 19°$, then

$$\mu = \frac{\sin 30°}{\sin 19°}$$

from tables $\mu = \dfrac{0.500}{0.333} = 1.5$

The values of i and r measured in the last experiment can be used to calculate values of the refractive index air to glass. μ for air to glass is about 1·5, from air to water 1·33 and for air to diamond 2·4. There are different types of glass with

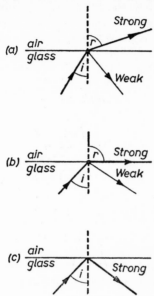

FIG. 12.12. CRITICAL ANGLE AND TOTAL INTERNAL REFLECTION

different refractive indices. These differences are made use of in constructing the most effective lens systems for optical instruments.

Critical Angle. We have seen that when a ray of light crosses a boundary into a less dense medium, e.g. from glass to air, it is refracted away from the normal. In addition a small proportion of the light is *reflected* back into the glass (Fig. 12.12 (*a*)). For the refracted ray the angle of refraction is always greater than the angle of incidence at the boundary. As this angle of incidence is increased a point is reached where the angle of refraction is equal to 90°, i.e. the ray emerging along the surface of the glass as shown in Fig. 12.12 (*b*). If the angle of incidence is now slightly increased the ray is unable to escape from the glass and the whole of it is reflected back into the glass (Fig. 12.12 (c)).

The angle of incidence at which all the light first becomes reflected is known as the *critical angle* and this reflection back into the denser medium is known as *total internal reflection*. The critical angle between glass and air is about 42°, and between water and air is about 49°.

Total internal reflection can be strikingly demonstrated by projecting a narrow beam of light into one end of a spiral of

FIG. 12.13. TOTAL INTERNAL REFLECTION DEMONSTRATED BY
SPIRAL OF GLASS ROD

glass rod as shown in Fig. 12.13. The light is unable to escape through the sides of the rod, being totally internally reflected many times before it emerges as a beam at the other end. Another interesting effect to consider is the view which a fish gets of the world above the water including his enemy the fisherman (Fig. 12.14).

Total reflection prisms are made use of in cameras (Fig. 12.15), binoculars, microscopes, telescopes, periscopes, and many other optical instruments.

We have seen that light passing through a rectangular glass block is refracted twice so that the ray emerging is actually going in the same direction as when it entered the glass, although it is displaced. The amount of displacement depends on the angle of incidence and on the thickness of the block (Fig. 12.16). If the incident ray is at right angles to the surface

of the water, looking ... it in actual dimensions, the
source of the ray appears ... to the observer. You can
quickly observe this if you place a rectangular glass ... look
in this look into it. ...

Prisms ...
through ... reflection prism ... ... not ... ...

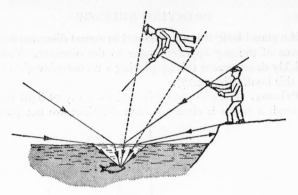

FIG. 12.14

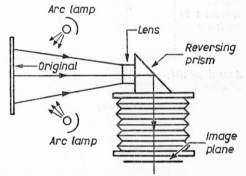

FIG. 12.15. A TOTAL REFLECTION PRISM IN A CAMERA

Arc lamp
Lens
Reversing prism
Original
Arc lamp
Image plane

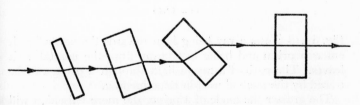

FIG. 12.16. DISPLACEMENT OF A RAY

155

of the glass block, it is not changed in actual direction but the source of the ray appears nearer to the observer. You can quickly demonstrate this by placing a rectangular glass block on this book (Fig. 12.17).

Prisms. The direction followed by a ray of light passing through a prism is changed since the sides are not parallel.

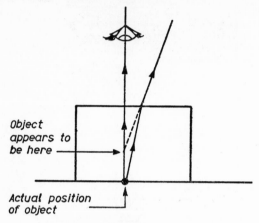

Object appears to be here ——→

Actual position of object ———

FIG. 12.17

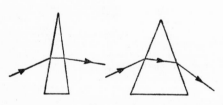

FIG. 12.18

Fig. 12.18 shows a ray being bent towards the normal as it enters a prism and being bent away from the normal as it leaves. The path of a ray of light through a prism can be traced by the method used in Experiment 2.

The greater the angle of a prism, the more refraction will take place (Fig. 12.18).

If two identical thin prisms are placed with their bases
together then pairs of parallel rays striking the prisms at equal
distances from their bases are refracted equally to meet on the
principal axis (Fig. 12.19).

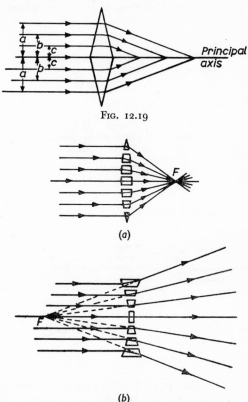

FIG. 12.19

(a)

(b)

FIG. 12.20. RAYS PASSING THROUGH LENSES

Lenses. The principle of the lens is understood if you
consider a series of matched prisms and blocks of glass. In
Fig. 12.20 (a) the parallel rays are refracted by different
amounts so that they all meet at one point F on the axis. In

Fig. 12.20 (*b*) the rays diverge as if they had all come from the point *F* on the axis. In each case the ray travelling along the principal axis is not refracted since the central glass block has parallel sides.

An actual lens is not built up from a series of prisms but is

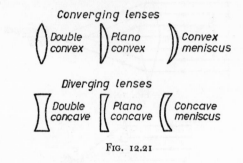

Converging lenses

Double convex   Plano convex   Convex meniscus

Diverging lenses

Double concave   Plano concave   Concave meniscus

FIG. 12.21

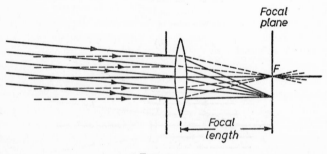

Focal plane

F

Focal length

FIG. 12.22

a solid piece of glass ground so that each face forms part of a sphere. Six common types of lenses are shown in Fig. 12.21.

Convex Lenses. When rays of light parallel to the principal axis fall on to the central area of a convex lens, they converge to meet on the axis at a point *F*, known as the *principal focus* (*see* Fig. 12.22). The distance from the centre of the lens to *F* is a constant for any lens or system of lenses known as its *focal length*.

The diagram also shows another set of rays, not parallel to the axis. They converge on the *focal plane* of the lens.

EXPERIMENT 3. TO FIND AN APPROXIMATE VALUE OF THE FOCAL LENGTH OF A CONVEX LENS

Move a convex lens in front of a piece of paper so as to obtain a sharp image of a large well-illuminated distant object, e.g. a window or some object outside. Measure the distance between the lens and the paper. Since the rays from a distant object are almost parallel, the measured distance will give an approximate value of the focal length of the lens.

The greater the curvature of the two surfaces of a lens, the shorter is its focal length. Every lens has two principal foci, one on either side of the lens at the same distance from its centre. Although a camera lens usually consists of two or more lenses combined together in order to improve the quality of the image, the lens system still has a simple focal length.

Ray Diagrams. The position of a clear image formed by a convex lens depends on the distance from the lens to the object and on the focal length of the lens. By choosing a suitable scale and drawing a ray diagram it is quite a simple matter to work out the approximate position of the focused image. It is usual to represent the object by a line perpendicular to the principal axis with an arrow head. Two rays are sufficient to fix the position of the image. We can assume that a thin lens is used and that the rays of light are near to being parallel to the axis. It follows that the ray passing through the centre of the lens will not be appreciably refracted. Secondly, we know that a ray from the object which is parallel to the axis will pass through the principal focus.

Fig. 12.23 shows an object placed between one and two focal lengths from the lens. The ray OA drawn parallel to the axis passes through the principal focus F_1, whilst the ray OC passing through the centre of the lens is not refracted. The two rays meet at I, the position of the image in focus. Notice that in this case the image is *magnified*, *inverted*, and *real*, i.e. it can be thrown on to a screen. Try drawing the object outside two focal lengths, i.e. beyond F_2'. You will find that the image is now *real*, *inverted*, and *reduced* in size. If the object is placed at F_2' the image is *real*, *inverted*, and the same size. If it is placed inside one focal length the lens is now functioning as a magnifying glass or magnifier (Fig. 12.24), carried in the pocket of many printers. In this case the image is formed on

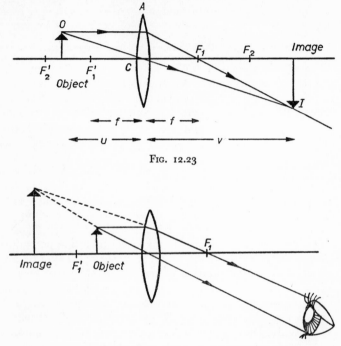

Fig. 12.23

Fig. 12.24. The Convex Lens as a Magnifying Glass

the same side of the lens as the object, cannot be screened and is called *virtual*.

Although there is this graphical method of calculating the position and size of an image it obviously need not be very accurate or convenient. A more satisfactory way of getting information is by substitution in equations connecting u, v, M, and f (Fig. 12.23) where u = the distance from the object to the lens (i.e. the copyboard distance on a camera),

v = the distance from the image to the lens (i.e. the camera extension),

f = the focal length of the lens, and

M = linear magnification = $\dfrac{\text{linear size of image}}{\text{linear size of object}}$

The equations are—

$$\frac{1}{u} + \frac{1}{v} = \frac{1}{f} \qquad \cdot \qquad \cdot \qquad \cdot \qquad \cdot \quad (1)$$

$$M = \frac{v}{u} \qquad \cdot \qquad \cdot \qquad \cdot \qquad \cdot \quad (2)$$

by combining these two equations it is possible to derive two further equations which are useful—

$$v = f(1 + M) \qquad \cdot \qquad \cdot \qquad \cdot \quad (3)$$

$$u = f\left(1 + \frac{1}{M}\right) \qquad \cdot \qquad \cdot \qquad \cdot \quad (4)$$

Given any two of the four terms it is possible to calculate the remaining two by substituting in the appropriate equations, e.g.

1. Where will the image showing a magnification of two be formed by a lens of focal length 18 in.?

$$M = 2$$
$$f = 18 \text{ in.}$$
$$v = f(1 + M)$$
$$v = 18\,(1 + 2)$$
$$v = 54 \text{ in.}$$

The image will be formed 54 in. from the lens (try checking this result by the graphical method).

2. An object 4 cm wide is placed 36 cm from a lens of focal length 12 cm. Where will the image be formed and what will be its width?

$$f = 12$$

$$u = 36$$

$$\frac{1}{u} + \frac{1}{v} = \frac{1}{f}$$

$$\frac{1}{v} = \frac{1}{f} - \frac{1}{u}$$

$$\frac{1}{v} = \frac{1}{12} - \frac{1}{36} = \frac{3-1}{36} = \frac{2}{36}$$

$$v = 18 \text{ cm}$$

$$M = \frac{v}{u} = \frac{18}{36} = \frac{1}{2}$$

$$M = \frac{\text{linear size of image}}{\text{linear size of object}}$$

$$\frac{1}{2} = \frac{\text{width of image}}{4}$$

Width of image = 2 cm. Image is formed 18 cm from the lens

EXPERIMENT 4. To DETERMINE THE FOCAL LENGTH OF A CONVEX LENS

Apparatus. Light box; simple optical bench; large screen; convex lens lens holder.

Set up the apparatus as shown in Fig. 12.25, fixing the position of the light-box object and the screen. Move the lens until a clear inverted image is obtained on the screen. Measure the u and v distances and substituting in the equation

$$\frac{1}{u} + \frac{1}{v} = \frac{1}{f},$$

calculate the focal length of the lens. Measure the object and image height and calculate the magnification from the equation—

$$M = \frac{\text{linear size of image}}{\text{linear size of object}}$$

Compare this value with the ratio $\frac{v}{u}$.

Notice that for any position of object and screen there are two positions of the lens which will give a clear image. The u distance in the first position becomes the v distance in the second and vice versa. The pairs of points where object and image are interchangeable are called conjugate foci.

Repeat the experiment changing the distance from light box to screen and finding new u and v distances. In each case calculate f and finally work out an average value.

The focal length of a camera lens is usually found by a simpler method. The camera is adjusted to give a same-size

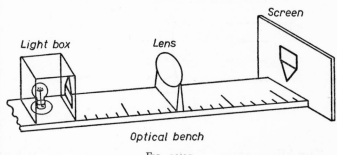

FIG. 12:25

image of a foot rule or similar graduated scale and the position of a point on the rack of the camera is marked. The camera is now set to give a half-size image and a second mark is made. The distance d between the two marks is measured and is equal to half the focal length of the lens.

$$v = f(1 + M). \qquad . \qquad . \qquad . \qquad (3)$$

In same-size position—

$$v_1 = f(1 + 1) = 2f$$

In half-size position—

$$v_2 = f(1 + \tfrac{1}{2}) = 1\tfrac{1}{2}f$$

$$d = v_1 - v_2 = 2f - 1\tfrac{1}{2}f = \tfrac{1}{2}f$$

Concave Lenses. If a beam of parallel rays falls on the central area of a concave lens the rays diverge (Fig. 12.26). If the refracted rays are produced back they meet on the lens axis at a point F, the principal focus. The distance from the lens to F is the focal length of the lens.

Draw a ray diagram to show how an image is formed of an object placed between one and two focal lengths. Is this image virtual or real, upright or inverted, magnified or reduced?

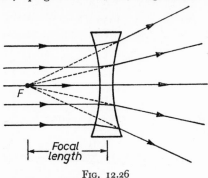

Focal length

FIG. 12.26

The Microscope. The microscope is used extensively to examine printing surfaces, paper and print, particularly in the investigation of production problems.

It consists of two lenses or lens combinations, an eyepiece lens and an objective lens (Fig. 12.27). The objective lens forms an inverted real image I_1 of an object placed just outside its focal length. This image is then viewed by the eyepiece lens acting as a simple magnifying glass. A greatly enlarged virtual image is formed at I_2. To learn how to make effective use of a microscope it is suggested that you study the appropriate sections in one of the books by F. D. Armitage and by L. G. Luker mentioned at the end of this chapter.

A relatively low-powered binocular microscope has proved itself to be particularly suitable for looking at the surfaces of paper, prints, and printing surfaces in the investigation of printing problems. One of these instruments is included on the PATRA test bench. A binocular microscope is essentially a combination of two microscopes, one for each eye, giving the image a three-dimensional appearance.

Cameras, magnifiers, and microscopes are not the only important optical arrangements being used in printing.

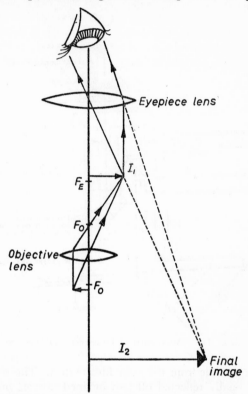

FIG. 12.27. THE PRINCIPLE OF THE MICROSCOPE

Optical systems have been devised for the photographic composition of letters on film.

The system used in the "Monophoto" filmsetter is shown in Fig. 12.28. The character to be photographed is positioned under the light source and a shutter device operates at a normal exposure speed of one-fiftieth of a second. The light passes through an optical wedge and then through a lens and two sets of prisms whose positions can be varied to give whatever magnification is required. Type sizes of 6 to 24

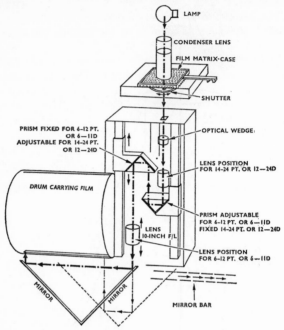

FIG. 12.28. THE "MONOPHOTO" FILMSETTER OPTICAL SYSTEM

point are possible from the same film matrix. The character image is finally reflected off two inclined mirrors on to the film carried on a drum. Wherever the mirrors are placed, the distance from the lens to film remains the same, thus giving constant definition as the characters are successively projected.

THINGS TO LEARN

1. Light travels in straight lines.

2. The *Inverse Square Law* of light states that the intensity of

illumination E over a surface due to a point source of light decreases as the square of the distance d from the lamp.

3. When a ray of light is reflected from a smooth surface, the angle of incidence is equal to the angle of reflection, and the reflected ray is always in the same plane as the incident ray. The image formed by a plane mirror is the same size as the object and is in a position as far behind the reflecting surface as the object is in front.

4. Light crossing the boundary between any two different transparent media is bent or refracted. The ratio of the sines of the angle of the angles of incidence i and refraction r is a constant for any pair of these materials. The constant is called the refractive index (μ).

$$\mu = \frac{\sin i}{\sin r}$$

5. The equations connecting the focal length f, the magnification M, the image distance v and the object distance u for a lens are—

$$\frac{1}{u} + \frac{1}{v} = \frac{1}{f}$$

$$M = \frac{v}{u}$$

$$v = f(1 + M)$$

$$u = f\left(1 + \frac{1}{M}\right)$$

OTHER BOOKS TO READ

L. S. POWELL, *Elementary Physics for Technical Students* (Pitman)

L. G. LUKER, *Science for Printers* (Griffin)

M. NELKON, *Principles of Physics*, Part II "Heat, Light, and Sound" (Christophers)

F. D. ARMITAGE, *An Atlas of Paper Fibres, An Introduction to Paper Microscopy* (Guildhall)

H. M. CARTWRIGHT, *Graphic Arts Manual* (Ilford)

EXERCISES

1. Show the connexion between wavelength and frequency. What is the frequency of visible red light with a wavelength of 700 mμ? (velocity of light = approx. 300,000,000 metres per second).

2. (a) Give a reasoned explanation of the "inverse square law of light." (b) A table is lighted by an electric bulb suspended 4 ft perpendicularly above it; calculate the relative intensity of illumination when the lamp is 7 ft perpendicularly above the table. (c) State reasons for thinking that the calculated value is only approximately correct. (Photo/1958/Int.)

3. Explain the meaning of the terms wavelength, transparent, translucent, opaque, beam, and ray.

4. (a) If the correct exposure of a negative is $4\frac{1}{2}$ min at 3 ft, how long would the exposure be if the frame were moved back to 5 ft?

(b) Why might it become necessary to move back the lamp?

(Litho/1961/Fin.)

5. With the aid of diagrams explain what happens when light falls on (a) a glossy white paper surface; and (b) a matt white paper surface.

6. Define: (a) specular reflection; (b) diffuse reflection.

What are the laws of reflection and the characteristics of an image formed by a plane mirror?

7. Explain the principles of reflection and refraction, illustrating your remarks with the aid of a diagram showing parallel light falling on a bi-convex lens and coming to a focus. (Photo/1961/Int.)

8. (a) Draw diagrams, with explanatory notes, showing the path of a ray of light passing from air through glass when it falls: (i) at an angle on a parallel sided sheet of glass; (ii) at an angle to the axis of a biconvex lens. (b) In the case of the lens, show the direction the ray would take if the surrounding medium were water. (Photo/1956/Fin.)

9. Explain the meaning of refractive index, total internal reflection, and dispersion.

10. Describe a workshop method of finding the focal length of a camera lens.

11. Draw ray diagrams to show the formation of an image by a convex lens with the object placed (a) outside two focal lengths; (b) between one and two focal lengths; (c) inside one focal length. How do these images differ?

12. Calculate the object and image distance when an 18-in. lens is used or copying (a) same size; (b) three-quarter size; and (c) one-quarter size. (Photo/1960/Int.)

13. (a) Show by sketching selected light rays how the simple magnifying glass produces a magnified image, indicating clearly the position of the object, its image and the focal points.

(b) What is meant by a magnification of "four diameters"?

(c) A print is viewed through a convex lens held one inch from it. If the focal length of the lens is two inches, how much larger will the print appear? Will the print appear inverted?

(d) In order to project an image of the print on to a screen with the above lens, what alteration would be necessary in the position of it relative to the print? Illustrate with a ray diagram. (FTC/1960.)

CHAPTER 13

COLOUR

Ordinary White Light is a Mixture of Coloured Lights. This was the great discovery made by Newton 300 years ago when he placed a glass prism in the path of a narrow pencil of sunlight coming through a hole in the blind of a darkened room. The white light was split up into a band

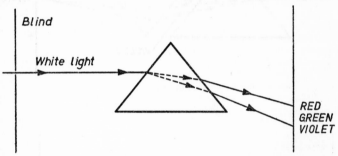

Fig. 13.1

of colours ranging from red, through green to violet, and these he projected on to a screen (Fig. 13.1).

He found that when he placed an identical prism in an inverted position between the first prism and the screen, the light on the screen was almost white. The band of coloured lights had recombined to give white light again (Fig. 13.2).

If the second prism was not inverted the same band of colours fell on the screen, but they were spread over a greater distance (Fig. 13.3).

These experiments led Newton to think that white light is composed of seven colours which are red, orange, yellow, green, blue, indigo, and violet. In fact, since the colours change continuously across the band, there are as many colours as you can find names to describe them. The complete range of colours from red to violet is called the *visible spectrum*.

Have a look at a small light source through a prism in a darkened room. Make a note of the colours that you are able to distinguish.

We have already seen how light is bent or refracted when its path crosses a boundary between two different transparent

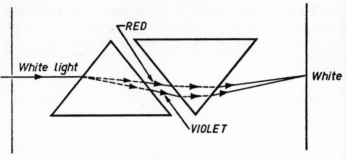

FIG. 13.2

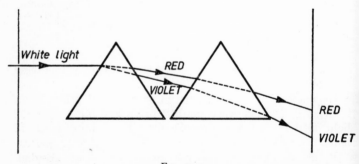

FIG. 13.3

substances like air and glass or glass and water. Newton's experiments made it clear that, when a beam of white light is refracted at such a boundary, the coloured lights in the mixture are bent by different amounts. In other words, the refractive index of a particular type of glass is different for the various colours in the spectrum (Table 7).

Table 7
TABLE SHOWING THE REFRACTIVE INDEX OF TWO TYPES OF GLASS FOR DIFFERENT COLOURED LIGHTS

| | Colour | | | | | |
Substance	Violet	Blue	Green	Yellow	Orange	Red
Crown glass	1·538	1·531	1·526	1·523	1·522	1·520
Dense flint glass	1·698	1·684	1·674	1·667	1·665	1·662

The spread of colour produced by the passage of white light through a prism is called *dispersion* (Fig. 13.4).

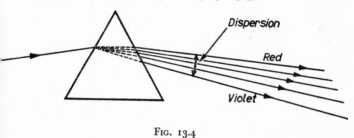

Fig. 13.4

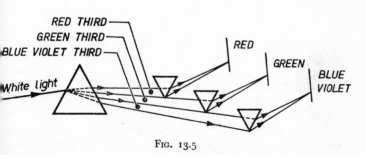

Fig. 13.5

Primary Colours. If we divide the visible spectrum into three equal parts and blend the colours in each third we get blue-violet, green, and red (Fig. 13.5).

These are known as the *primary light colours*, since any colour can be matched by mixing these three coloured lights in the correct proportions.

Additive Colour. Colour produced by the addition of beams of coloured light is known as *additive colour*. The effect of adding the three primary colours can be demonstrated in a number of ways.

The colour triangle is a flat triangular-shaped board with a housed lamp at each of the corners, throwing light through

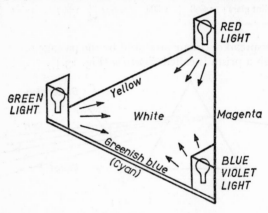

FIG. 13.6. THE COLOUR TRIANGLE

the windows facing the board. If glass or gelatin colour filters are slotted into these windows, coloured lights are mixed in different proportions at different points on the board. If the three filters of the primary colours, green, red, and blue-violet, are used, every possible colour should appear somewhere on the surface of the triangle (Fig. 13.6). In practice, this is not possible because the primary filters never transmit exactly one-third of the spectrum. Nevertheless, a great many colours are produced.

In the centre of the triangle the three primaries mix equally to give white light. Half-way down each side you see the result of mixing the primary lights in pairs: bluish-red

PLATE I

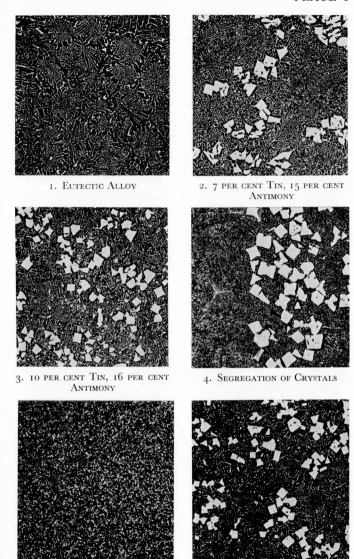

1. EUTECTIC ALLOY

2. 7 PER CENT TIN, 15 PER CENT
ANTIMONY

3. 10 PER CENT TIN, 16 PER CENT
ANTIMONY

4. SEGREGATION OF CRYSTALS

5. EFFECT OF FAST COOLING

6. EFFECT OF SLOW COOLING

(*All photomicrographs magnified* ×67, *supplied by Fry's Metal Foundries Ltd.*)

PLATE II

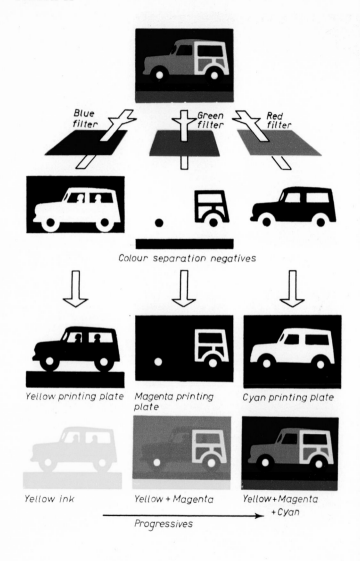

Blue filter   Green filter   Red filter

Colour separation negatives

Yellow printing plate   Magenta printing plate   Cyan printing plate

Yellow ink   Yellow + Magenta   Yellow + Magenta + Cyan

Progressives

PLATE III

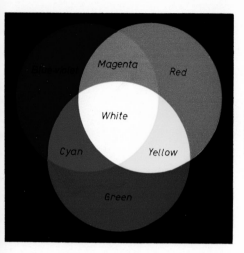

ADDITIVE COLOUR

Overlapping beams of the primary lights, blue-violet, red and green, projected on to a white screen. Each beam *adds* one-third of the visible spectrum.

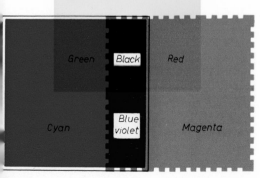

SUBTRACTIVE COLOUR

Overlapping prints of the pigment primaries, cyan, magenta and yellow, on white paper. Each print *subtracts* one-third of the visible spectrum from the white light reflected from the paper.

TRI-COLOUR PRINTING

PLATE IV

1. MACHINE FINISHED PAPER (×8)

2. SURFACE SIZED CARTRIDGE PAPER (×8)

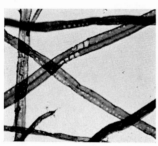

3. CHEMICAL WOOD (×82)

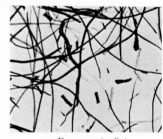

4. ESPARTO (×82)

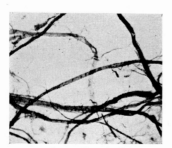

5. LINEN RAG (×82)

6. MECHANICAL WOOD (×82)

(Photomicrographs supplied by PATRA)

(magenta) between blue and red, greenish-blue (cyan) between blue and green, and yellow between red and green. These are sometimes known as the secondary light colours.

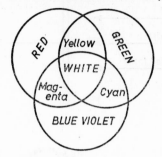

FIG. 13.7

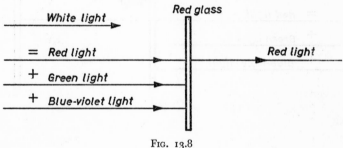

FIG. 13.8

Similar effects can be obtained by projecting beams of red, green, and blue-violet lights from three projection lamps (Fig. 13.7). This is shown in colour Plate III.

Selective Absorption. If you hold a piece of red glass in a beam of white light, preferably sunlight, it will throw a beam of red light on to a screen. In other words, the glass is stopping green and blue-violet light and only letting through the red third of the spectrum (Fig. 13.8).

Similarly a piece of green glass would absorb blue-violet and red and transmit the green third of the spectrum (Fig. 13.9).

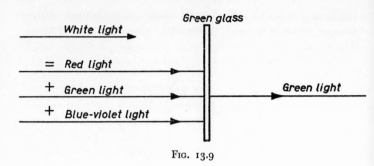

Green glass

White light

= Red light
+ Green light
+ Blue-violet light

Green light

FIG. 13.9

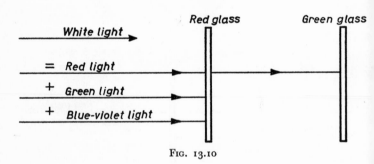

Red glass   Green glass

White light

= Red light
+ Green light
+ Blue-violet light

FIG. 13.10

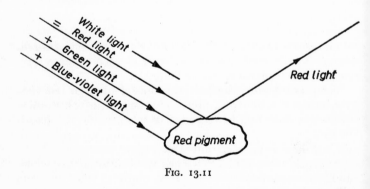

= White light
  Red light
+ Green light
+ Blue-violet light

Red light

Red pigment

FIG. 13.11

174

If both the green and the red glasses were placed in the beam of white light, no light would be able to pass through (Fig. 13.10).

Pieces of coloured glass or gelatin are called colour filters. They are able to select a part of the spectrum and absorb it, *transmitting* the remainder. In exactly the same way pigments in inks selectively absorb part of the white light and *reflect* the

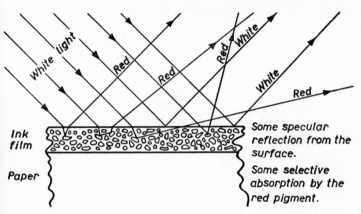

FIG. 13.12. LIGHT REFLECTED FROM A FILM OF RED INK

remainder. A red pigment absorbs green and blue-violet and reflects red (Fig. 13.11).

The pigments and dyes which give colour to printing inks, paints, plastics, filters, textiles, flowers, trees, and all plants are substances which are able to absorb selectively a part of the visible spectrum and reflect or transmit the remainder.

In a printing ink, the particles of pigment are surrounded by a transparent material, which will reflect some white light in the way that a mirror reflects light (specular reflection, Chapter 12).

If a print is varnished, so that the surface layer contains no pigment, then this type of reflection, which gives the effect we call gloss, is greatly increased.

Take a small piece of a dull coloured print on a pad of paper, place on one edge a drop of spirit varnish, and spread this evenly over part of the colour with a glass rod held at both ends (Fig. 13.13).

Notice how the gloss has changed in the varnished areas.

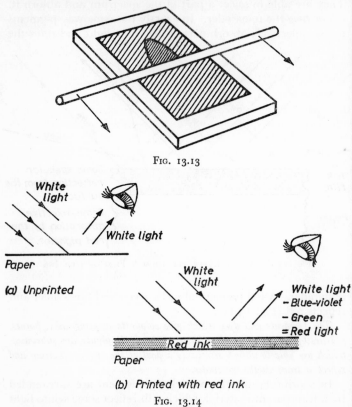

FIG. 13.13

White light

White light

Paper

(a) Unprinted

White light

White light
– Blue-violet
– Green
= Red light

Red ink

Paper

(b) Printed with red ink

FIG. 13.14

Subtractive Colour. With additive colour which we have already discussed, we start with an absence of light (black) and build up colours by adding coloured lights. The colour triangle is a practical demonstration of this method. In printing, we normally start with white paper. Since this reflects nearly all the white light falling on it, it is behaving like a "second-hand" source of white light. In applying an ink to its surface, we are not adding but *subtracting parts of the spectrum* from the white light coming to our eyes from the paper. Colour produced on a surface by adding inks or paints which selectively absorb a part of the spectrum is known as *subtractive colour*.

To take an example, if we print a red ink on to white paper, we are subtracting blue-violet and green from the reflected white light (Fig. 13.14).

Subtractive Primary Colours (Pigment primaries). The most useful primary colours for this subtractive method are pigment colours which each *absorb one-third* of the spectrum just as the additive primaries *add one-third* of the spectrum.

These *subtractive primary colours* are—

Greenish-blue or CYAN = White — Red (a pigment which absorbs the red third of the spectrum)

Bluish-red or MAGENTA = White — Green (a pigment which absorbs the green third of the spectrum)

YELLOW = White — Blue-violet (a pigment which absorbs the blue-violet third of the spectrum)

Let us now see what the effects are of printing transparent inks of these three colours on top of one another on white paper.

Before reading on or looking at Fig. 13.15, work out the colours that you would expect to be produced in the four positions of overlap.

Position 1

Cyan + Magenta
Since Cyan = White — Red, and
Magenta = White — Green
Then their combined effect will be
        White — Red — Green = Blue-violet

Position 2

Cyan + Yellow
Since Cyan = White − Red, and
Yellow = White − Blue-violet
Cyan + Yellow = White − Red − Blue-violet = Green

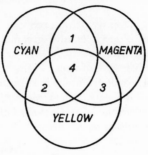

Fig. 13.15

Position 3

Magenta + Yellow
Since Magenta = White − Green, and
Yellow = White − Blue-violet
Magenta + Yellow = White − Green − Blue-violet = Red

Notice that the pigment primaries, taken two at a time give us pigment secondary colours, and bring us back to the light primaries. In the same way the light primaries, taken in pairs, gave us the pigment primaries (refer back to Figs. 13.6 and 13.7).

In position 4

Magenta + Yellow + Cyan
Magenta = White − Green
Yellow = White − Blue-violet
Cyan = White − red.
Magenta + Yellow + Cyan = White − Green −
Blue-violet − Red = Black

Now have a look at Plate III, which shows this in colour. You can demonstrate this in several ways—

(*a*) With transparent three-colour printing inks.

(*b*) With the three-colour water colours developed by PATRA (obtainable from Dane & Co.).

(*c*) Using a colour triangle with cyan, magenta, and yellow filters.

(*d*) Using these same filters to project three beams of cyan, magenta and yellow light on to a screen.

Three-colour Printing. Since the amount of *magenta* ink printed controls the quantity of *green* light coming to the eye, the amount of *cyan* ink controls the quantity of *red* light coming to the eye, and the amount of *yellow* ink controls the quantity of *blue-violet* light coming to the eye, in theory, it is possible to produce any colour on white paper using these three inks. This is the principle of *three-colour printing* (Plate II).

In half-tone printing, the dots of the three colours are not printed on top of one another, but in a uniform pattern alongside one another. The areas of the colours are so small that the eye is able to mix their effects to get an impression similar to that from superimposed transparent inks.

Unfortunately, in practice, the ideal pigments for three-colour inks do not exist, and this greatly complicates the job of the photo process worker. With the pigments which are available, it is not possible to produce every possible colour by this three-colour method. The nearest approaches to perfect tri-colour inks have been the subject of British Standards Specifications 1480 and 3020 for letterpress and 2650 for lithographic inks.

In Chapter 12 we saw that visible light is only a fraction of a vast range of electromagnetic waves. The eye is able to detect those rays with wavelengths between about 400 mμ and 700 mμ, and to get different colour responses from the various wavelengths in this band. Light with a wavelength of 400 mμ gives a violet response, wavelengths at 700 mμ appear red and in the middle of the visible spectrum at about 550 mμ they appear green. If the whole range from 400 to 700 mμ arrives together then we get the sensation of white light. Earlier in this chapter, we saw that the primary light colours consist of thirds of the spectrum. Considered on the wavelength scale these are approximately—

Blue-violet .	. 400 to 500 mμ
Green .	. 500 to 600 mμ
Red . .	. 600 to 700 mμ

Sources of Light. If you heat a poker in a fire it eventually becomes a dull red colour, then a brighter red and finally it may become "white hot." The type of coloured light given out has changed with the temperature. Nearly all light is produced by raising the temperature of a body until it becomes luminous. The most important of all our light sources, the outer layers of the sun, have an average temperature of over 5,000°C. A carbon arc lamp may reach a temperature of over 4,000°C. An ordinary light bulb contains a tungsten filament which will be heated to about 2,000°C. As one might expect with these varied temperatures the nature of light from these three sources is quite different. For instance, a tungsten lamp gives a much yellower light than either the carbon arc or sunlight. A mercury vapour lamp is rich in blue light and deficient at the yellow end of the spectrum. Even the nature of sunlight varies a good deal. The light from a blue sky has a very different composition from dawn sunlight. A knowledge of the spectral quality of light sources is important, since a coloured substance can only possibly reflect the colours that are falling on it. For example, the sodium lamp, frequently used for street lighting, gives off a pure yellow. This means that under this light any object which contains no yellow will appear black.

Spectral Reflection Curves. A convenient way of describing the colour of an ink on paper is a graph in which the percentage reflection is plotted against the wavelength of light (Fig. 13.16).

The curve for this particular ink indicates that it reflects strongly in the red third of the spectrum and in addition reflects a certain amount of blue. Notice that there is some reflection of all wavelengths. This is true for all reflection colours and is due to the general reflection from the white paper under the ink.

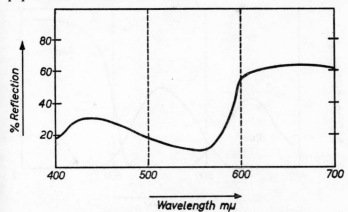

FIG. 13.16. SPECTRAL REFLECTION CURVE FOR A RED INK

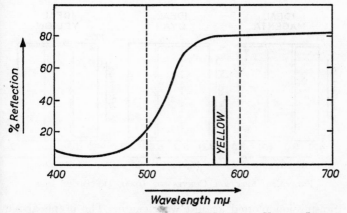

FIG. 13.17. SPECTRAL REFLECTION CURVE FOR A YELLOW INK

Notice that the curve for a typical yellow ink (Fig. 13.17) reflects a great deal of red and green in addition to the pure spectral yellow at about 560 to 580 mμ.

Spectral Transmission Curves. The same graphical method can be used to describe the nature of the light transmitted by colour filters. This time the graph is of percentage

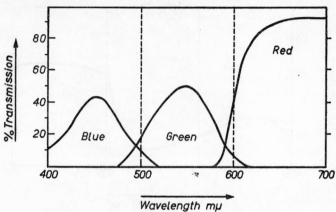

FIG. 13.18. SPECTRAL CURVES FOR THREE TYPICAL FILTERS

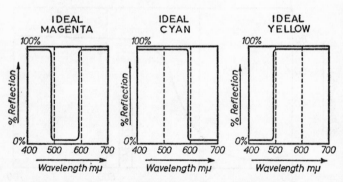

FIG. 13.19. SPECTRAL CURVES FOR IDEAL TRI-COLOUR INKS

transmission plotted against wavelength. The graph above shows the spectral curves for three typical filters for three-colour work (Fig. 13.18).

Spectral Curves for Three-colour Inks. We mentioned earlier that the ideal inks for the three-colour method of printing would each absorb one-third of the spectrum and reflect the remaining two-thirds. The spectral curves for these ideal inks would look like those in Fig. 13.19.

However, with the pigments available the nearest approach to these ideal inks is shown below in the curves of the standard letterpress inks B.S. 3020 (Fig. 13.20).

Colour Measurement. Most colour measurement is done with that remarkable instrument called the eye. Remarkable

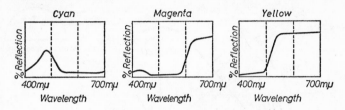

FIG. 13.20. SPECTRAL CURVES OF THE STANDARD LETTERPRESS INKS (B.S. 3020)

as it is, the eye has its limitations as a device for accurately describing a particular colour. No three eyes are the same, even if two sometimes are, and so it may be that a printer and his customer do not see "eye to eye" over the colour of a job. Exact measurements mean facts, and not opinions expressed on what you think you see. This is the background to the efforts which have been made to develop an instrument which could "look at a colour" and describe it in figures or in the form of a spectral curve on a graph. These efforts have met with a good deal of success.

A true *spectrophotometer* costs several thousands of pounds, is essentially a laboratory instrument and provides a precise means of measuring colour.

Photo-electric comparators (sometimes called spectrophotometers) are less expensive and more suited to industrial use. The results are not as precise as those from a spectrophotometer but they are adequate for many purposes. These comparators may be arranged to measure the reflected light from a print or transmitted light from a filter or film. The general principle of a reflection comparator is shown in Fig. 13.21.

Light from a small filament lamp is concentrated by a lens, passed through a filter and then on to the print at an angle of 45°. The filter lets through only a fraction of the visible spectrum. If any of this particular coloured light is reflected by the print, some of it will fall on the photo-electric cell placed directly over the print. The cell is put in this position

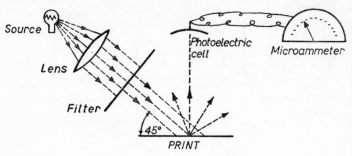

FIG. 13.21. A REFLECTION COMPARATOR

rather than at 45° so that any specular reflection from the print due to its gloss is not being collected. The cell will convert this light energy into a quantity of electrical energy which is given by the reading of the microammeter.

In use, the comparator is first placed on a standard white surface (normally a block of magnesium carbonate) which one assumes reflects 100 per cent of the light of all wavelengths. The microammeter is adjusted so that the scale reading is 100 units, and then the comparator is moved on to the print being examined. If the reading is only 20 units, this indicates that only one-fifth as much of the light passing through the filter is reflected by the print as reflected by the white surface. The colour filter is now replaced by a second which lets through another portion of the spectrum. The comparator is again standardized on the white block, and then a new reading is obtained for the print. This method is repeated with a range of filters which cover the whole spectrum. Knowing the band of wavelengths that each filter transmits, it is then possible to draw a graph of percentage reflection against wavelength, similar to those we discussed earlier in this chapter.

The usefulness of the result depends to a large extent on the quality of the filters and the number used. It is beyond the scope of this book to do more than mention colour measurement. Fuller information on the methods and applications of colour measurement in printing will be found in the books referred to at the end of this chapter.

COLOUR TERMINOLOGY (showing in brackets, some other commonly used terms)—

(i) *Hue.* "Colour" given by the dominant wavelength of radiations (colour, shade).

(ii) *Saturation* given by the presence in the colour of more or less white (strong, weak, rich, bright, pale).

(iii) *Lightness* given by the *amount* of light reflected or in other words by the amount of black in a body (tone, density, dark, light, deep, dim).

THINGS TO LEARN

1. Colour produced by the addition of coloured lights is known as *additive colour.* *Red, green,* and *blue-violet* are the *light primaries* or *additive primaries,* and by adding these three lights in various proportions it is possible to produce any colour.

2. Colour produced normally on a white surface by the addition of substances which selectively absorb (subtract) part of the visible spectrum and reflect the remainder is known as *subtractive colour.* *Cyan, magenta,* and *yellow* are the *subtractive primaries* or *pigment primaries,* and by adding these three pigments in various proportions it is possible to produce a very large range of colours.

OTHER BOOKS TO READ

V. LETOUZEY, *Colour and Colour Measurement in the Graphic Industries* (Pitman)
W. D. WRIGHT, *The Measurement of Colour* (Hilger & Watts)
H. M. CARTWRIGHT, *Graphic Arts Manual* (Ilford)

EXERCISES

1. Describe the use of a prism: (*a*) to secure a reversed image; (*b*) to produce a visible spectrum.   (Photo/1960/Int.)

2. Describe an experiment to examine the effects of mixing the primary light colours and list these effects.

3. Comment briefly on the statements that—

(a) "All colours in nature can be matched with suitable mixtures of red, green, and blue light."

(b) "Many colours can be matched with mixtures of yellow, magenta and cyan pigments." (Photo/1956/Fin.)

4. Using poster colours, construct a diagram to show: (a) the primary pigment colours; (b) the secondary pigment colours; (c) the pairs of complementary colours in (a) and (b). (Lp Mc/1959/Int.)

5. Explain the nature of selective colour absorption, illustrating your answer with diagrams showing: (a) the light transmitted by a green filter; and (b) the light reflected from a green print.

6. With the aid of poster colours make a diagram to show the primary pigment colours with their respective complementary colours.

(Lp Mc/1960/Int.)

7. (a) In talking about colour, explain the expression "Blue is white minus green and red." How would you describe green and red in a similar way?

(b) Explain in colorimetric terms the colours produced when a set of ideal trichromatic inks are superimposed in different combinations on white paper. Illustrate your answer with a diagram. (FTC/1960.)

8. (a) Draw typical curves of the spectral transmission of the following filters: tricolour red, green, and blue; light yellow; deep yellow.

(b) Draw a typical spectral density curve of the tricolour red filter.

(Photo/1959/Fin.)

9. Describe one type of photo-electric instrument used for the measurement of analysis of colour and state how it is used. (LpMc/1960/Fin.)

10. (a) Draw a diagram showing the position of yellow in the visible spectrum.

(b) Explain how spectral yellow could be matched visually with the aid of red and green filters.

(c) Draw a spectral transmission diagram of the red and green filters.

(d) Draw a spectral reflection diagram of a yellow pigment and of the same pigment diluted with white. (Photo/1961/Fin.)

CHAPTER 14

METALS FOR CASTING

METAL printing surfaces are usually prepared in one of two ways—by casting molten metal into the required form or by etching away unwanted parts of a solid plate of metal. For the casting process we need a metal which will melt at a fairly low temperature, give an accurate reproduction of type and illustration and also wear well on the printing machine. No single metal meets these conditions really satisfactorily so we use a combination of metals known as an *alloy*. Alloys are normally mixtures of two or more metals and the combination used for casting in the printing trade is lead, tin, and antimony.

Lead is a very soft and malleable metal with a specific gravity of 11·37 and melting point 621°F (327°C). It is much too soft to be used alone and as it contracts in solidifying it would not give the sharply defined casting needed for good printing.

Antimony is crystalline and brittle with specific gravity 6·71 and melting point 1,166°F (630°C). Its presence in the alloy gives it hardness and as antimony expands slightly in solidifying it improves the accuracy of the casting which is formed.

Tin, like lead, is soft and malleable but it has a much higher tensile strength. Its specific gravity is 7·29 and melting point 449·6°F (232°C). It toughens the alloy and in combination with the antimony improves its wearing quality.

Eutectic Alloy. When these metals are alloyed one dissolves in the other in varying degrees. In the same way as a solution of salt in water has a lower freezing point than pure water, so a solution of another metal in lead has a lower freezing point than pure lead. The lowest temperature at which a part of an alloy melts or freezes is called the *eutectic temperature*. This temperature remains the same whatever the proportions in which the particular group of metals is mixed. Melting or freezing of the alloy takes place over a range of temperature instead of at a fixed point. The part which melts first or solidifies last does so at the eutectic temperature.

If we start with a completely molten and thoroughly mixed combination of lead, tin, and antimony and cool the mixture slowly, three quite distinct stages will be seen. In the first stage the rate of cooling remains steady for as long as the whole of the mixture is liquid. When what is known as the *separation point* is reached the rate of cooling slows down and the second stage begins. During this stage part of the metal begins to solidify into crystals of tin, antimony, and combinations of the two, the nature of the crystals depending on the proportion of each metal present. At the end of stage two the loss of part of the metal in the form of crystals has brought the composition of the remaining molten metal to the composition at which it will solidify all together—that is, to the *eutectic alloy* which behaves as though it were a pure metal. The temperature now remains constant at the eutectic temperature until solidification is complete, when it will begin to fall steadily again as the now solid alloy cools to room temperature. For the lead, tin, and antimony alloys the composition of the eutectic alloy is 4 per cent tin, 12 per cent antimony, and 84 per cent lead. The eutectic temperature is 463°F.

EXPERIMENT 1. TO DRAW THE COOLING CURVE OF A PRINTING ALLOY

Apparatus. Large crucible; asbestos lagging; steel-cased thermometer; seconds timer.

Heat a quantity of mono or stereo metal in the crucible until the alloy is completely molten. Lag the crucible with asbestos packing and place the thermometer in the molten metal. Read the temperature at intervals of about 30 seconds and draw a graph with the temperature on the vertical axis and the time on the horizontal axis. The shape of the curve obtained should be similar to that shown in Fig. 5.6 on p. 58.

Printing Alloys. The hardness of a printing alloy depends on the amount of tin-antimony crystals formed during the second stage of cooling, so it is desirable to have a high proportion of these present. On the other hand the separation point rises with the amount of antimony present and thus the harder alloys have to be worked at a higher temperature. It is common practice, therefore, to use softer alloys in slug casting machines, harder ones in single letter casting and stereotyping. Some typical alloys and their melting ranges are—

| Composition (per cent) | | | Melting |
Tin	Antimony	Lead	Range °F
4	11	85	463–477
6	15	79	463–502
10	15	75	463–518
12	24	64	463–626

In each case the working temperature of the metal must be kept well above the separation point, because it has to remain completely molten for the whole journey from the melting pot to the face of the mould in which it is to be cast. If separation starts on the journey then the nozzles of the pouring apparatus will become choked and the machine will cease to function properly or, at the least, a poorly defined face will appear in the casting.

Where alloys contain more than 4 per cent tin and 12 per cent antimony the first crystals to separate out are composed of equal proportions of these two metals. The crystals are cubic in shape, very hard and much lighter than the molten metal around them. If the metal is held a long time in this semi-molten condition these crystals will float to the surface. A tin content of 4 per cent or less in an alloy with a high proportion of antimony reduces the tin content of the separating crystals to about 10 per cent. This type of crystal is long and narrow but it behaves very similarly to the cubic type mentioned earlier. When the tin and antimony content of an alloy falls below the eutectic composition, the first metal to solidify out will be lead, which will tend to sink to the bottom of the mixture because its specific gravity is higher than that of the surrounding liquid.

Crystal Formation. All printing alloys, except the softest ones used on slug casting machines, are essentially made up of a large number of tin-antimony crystals held together by the eutectic alloy around them acting as a cement. A large number of small crystals evenly distributed through the eutectic will give a more homogeneous and better wearing material than a small number of large crystals with large areas of the soft eutectic exposed in between. The size of the crystals formed depends mainly on the rate of cooling. Slow cooling allows the crystals time to grow large and to concentrate in the upper part of the casting. Fast cooling gives small crystals closely packed together and evenly distributed through the casting.

The structure of a casting can best be examined with a microscope giving ×100 magnification and illumination which falls vertically on the specimen. The casting is cut with a metal saw and the exposed surface polished with successively finer grades of emery cloth, then powdered alumina and finally with a soft cloth. To increase the contrast between the white tin-antimony crystals and the darker eutectic the polished face is immersed in a 5 per cent solution of silver nitrate, the excess solution being washed off with water. The kind of structure found in various printing alloys is shown in Plate I facing page 172.

EXPERIMENT 2. TO COMPARE THE EFFECT OF FAST AND SLOW COOLING ON A PRINTING ALLOY

Apparatus. Crucible; two small ingot moulds; hacksaw; microscope with vertical illumination.

Melt the metal in the crucible and when fully molten pour into the two moulds, one of which is water cooled and the other thickly lagged with asbestos. Cut each ingot in two places, one near the top and the other near the bottom of each casting. The exposed faces should be marked to avoid confusion at a later stage. The faces should then be prepared for microscopic examination as described above and the specimens compared under ×100 magnification. If the microscope has an eyepiece scale the sizes of the crystals seen can be measured.

Oxidation Losses. Printing alloys are melted down after use and used again. During the remelting some of the metal is oxidized and floats to the surface of the alloy as a fine powder called dross. If the remelting is carried out at the right temperature for the particular alloy concerned the loss is only from 0·05 per cent to 3 per cent of the total weight of metal. In most of the alloys, however, the proportion of tin oxidized is higher than the average for the metal as a whole, while the amount of antimony oxidized is below the average. Constant remelting would lead to a serious change in the overall composition of the alloy, particularly a loss of tin, which is called depreciation of the alloy. It is customary, therefore, to add a small amount of metal with more than the normal proportion of tin at each remelting to maintain the tin content at its proper level. In addition, the metal is *assayed*, that is, its composition is measured, from time to time so that exactly the right amount of each metal may be added to bring their proportions back to the right figure. Most metal suppliers offer a free assay service to their customers.

Impurities. The most common impurities which find their way into printing alloys during remelting are zinc and copper, dissolved into the alloy during remelting from scraps of brass rule, zinc, or copper plates. The ease with which zinc oxidizes causes the formation of a skin of oxide on the surface of the molten alloy. This skin, which is very strong, will lead to heavy losses of metal in the dross. Zinc also reduces the fluidity of the molten alloy and prevents it from flowing properly into the tiny crevices of the mould during casting. Presence of zinc in an alloy shows itself by very rapid dulling of the surface when the top of a batch or molten metal is skimmed. Little more than 0·001 per cent of zinc is needed to affect a printing alloy.

In very small quantities copper does not seriously affect printing alloys and it is sometimes added deliberately to typefounders' alloys to increase their hardness. But at the comparatively low temperatures used in sorts and slug casting, crystals of copper and antimony combined freeze out before the rest of the alloy begins to solidify. Such crystals choke the outlets from the metal pots and impede the flow of metal to the mould. Nickel is a less common impurity with a similar effect on the alloy to that of copper. Its effects become obvious, however, when about a hundredth of one per cent is present.

THINGS TO LEARN

1. The lowest temperature at which a portion of an alloy melts or freezes is called the eutectic temperature.

2. The composition of the part of the alloy melting at the eutectic temperature is always the same and is called the eutectic alloy.

3. Rapid cooling leads to the formation of small tin-antimony crystals but slow cooling gives a smaller number of large crystals.

4. Because proportionately more tin is oxidized than lead and antimony there is a fall in tin content at each remelting of a printing alloy unless more tin is added.

OTHER BOOKS TO READ

Printing Metals (Fry's Metal Foundries, Ltd.)
Printing Metals (Pass Printing Metals (London), Ltd.)

EXERCISES

1. What qualities do lead, antimony, and tin impart individually to stereo metal?   (E and S/1958/Int.)

2. With the aid of diagrams compare cooling curves for pure lead and a mono alloy, explaining the stage of solidification represented by each part of the curves.

3. What information is obtained from the cooling curve of a stereo metal?   (E and S/1959/Fin.)

4. What are the effects of the following impurities in a stereo metal: (*a*) copper; (*b*) zinc; (*c*) nickel?   (E and S/1958/Fin.)

5. How would you prepare a specimen of type metal for examination of its structure by a microscope? What main difference would you expect to find between two specimens of the same alloy if one had been rapidly cooled and the other slowly cooled?

CHAPTER 15

METALS FOR PLATEMAKING

ALTHOUGH there are altogether about eighty metals, only a few of them have the properties which are required in a printing plate. A metal for platemaking must be malleable with good wear resistance, a suitably fine grain structure, a reasonably high melting point, and the ability to be easily etched. There are four metals which have proved themselves in platemaking: these are copper, zinc, aluminium, and magnesium. We will first compare their specific gravities, their hardness and their melting points, and then taking them separately consider their other properties and their uses in the printing industry.

Specific Gravity. Table 8 shows the specific gravity of each of the four metals, together with those of iron, lead, and gold. You will see that zinc and copper are both fairly "heavy metals" whilst aluminium and magnesium are among the lightest of all metals. The specific gravity of a metal can be increased slightly by a mechanical treatment such as rolling or hammering, e.g. the s.g. of aluminium may vary from 2·58 to 2·69.

Table 8
SPECIFIC GRAVITY

Metal	Magnesium	Aluminium	Zinc	Iron	Copper	Lead	Gold
Specific gravity	1·7	2·6	7·1	7·8	8·6	11·4	19·3

Hardness. Hardness is related to wear resistance. Obviously it is a more important property for the metals used in making letterpress blocks than for aluminium and zinc plates in offset lithography (Table 9). In the past it was generally believed that the hardness of blocks increased greatly during the press run. An experiment conducted by PATRA has shown that the increases in hardness are quite small particularly when they are compared with the decreases liable to occur in the blockmaking process. The results of this investigation, carried out on a Miehle using a machine coated paper and black ink, are given in Table 10.

Table 9
HARDNESS

Metal	Zinc	Alu-minium	Mag-nesium	Copper	Nickel	Chro-mium
(Brinell) Hard-ness number	10	16	35	35	60	100

Table 10

Operation	% Hardness change		
	Copper	Magnesium	Zinc
A Blockmaking . . .	−2·6	−23·2	−5·3
B 89,000 impressions . .	−2·3	+0·6	+0·8
C Further 61,000 impressions with increased pressure	+3·3	+1·4	+0·3
Net effect of B and C .	+0·9	+2·0	+1·1

The mechanical properties of all metals including their hardness depend to a great extent on their purity and their physical condition. Generally speaking the more a metal is purified the softer it becomes. Mechanical properties and also corrosion resistance can often be improved by blending the metal with another metal or non-metal in an *alloy*. For instance gold for coinage is hardened by 8·3 per cent of copper and the presence of a small percentage of carbon converts iron into steel. The physical condition of a metal depends on whether it is "as cast" or whether it has been worked in some way. For example, the hardness of copper is greatly increased by rolling.

Melting Point. Table 11 shows the melting points of the platemaking metals. Notice that the melting point of zinc is low and very near to the burning-in temperature of fish glue which is believed to be between 350°C and 375°C. This and the fact that zinc is not dimensionally stable at temperatures as low as 200°C make the metal difficult to process.

Table 11
MELTING POINT

Metal	Zinc	Magnesium	Aluminium	Copper
Melting point.	419°C	651°C	657°C	1,062°C

A PATRA investigation into the effects of temperature on the hardness of blockmaking metals found that when magnesium was processed at 300°C its hardness fell by 15 per cent and that of zinc by 12 per cent. On the other hand the hardness of copper was not seriously affected until 400°C was exceeded. The report concludes that the maximum safe temperatures are 400°C for copper before hardness decreases, 250°C for magnesium before it becomes brittle, and 200°C for zinc. It suggests that some form of temperature control should be introduced in metal printing and the use of PVA (polyvinyl alcohol) or shellac coatings with lower burning-in temperatures be considered, particularly for zinc and magnesium.

COPPER

Copper is used for fine line and half-tone blocks for letterpress and for gravure plates and cylinders. Although these are its most vital jobs, it has other uses within the industry. It is used in bimetallic litho plates, for coating steel ink rollers, and in electrotypes for duplicate relief plates.

The most outstanding property of copper is its high conductivity of heat and electricity. Notice in Table 12 that

Table 12

Metal	Copper	Aluminium	Zinc	Magnesium	Silver	Iron	Lead
Relative electrical conductivity . (copper = 100)	100	62	29	39	106	17	8
Relative thermal conductivity . (copper = 100)	100	56	29	41	108	17	9

only silver is better in this respect. The world uses over three million tons of copper each year and about half of this is made into wire to carry electricity. Copper is both malleable and ductile. Foil less than $\frac{1}{500}$ in. thick and wire $\frac{1}{1000}$ in. in diameter are commercially produced. The metal has a fine crystalline structure so that very small dots in relief can be produced on and very fine cells etched into its surface.

Copper can be deposited electrolytically in thick or thin layers on to the surface of another metal (Chapter 18). Gravure cylinders often consist of a skin of copper laid down in this way on to a steel core. The physical condition of the coating may be varied by altering the conditions such as bath concentration, temperature, etc.

We have already seen that copper has a reasonable hardness, but its actual press life will depend to a great extent on the operating conditions. Wear resistance can be improved if necessary by putting on a facing of a harder metal, usually chromium.

Copper and Bimetallic Plates. The basic principle of lithography is to have image areas which are grease or ink receptive and non-image areas which repel ink. A deep-etch litho plate has an image consisting of a hard lacquer covered with a greasy ink, and a non-image area consisting of grained zinc or aluminium carrying a thin coating of water (Fig 15.1). Whilst these plates are extremely effective for runs up to 100,000, they cannot be expected to cope with the very long runs of over a million. Bimetallic and trimetallic plates have been

developed to print runs of this size. A bimetallic plate is one
which has one metal for the image and a different metal for
the non-image areas. Water does not wet all metals with the
same ease. The early approach to the problem was to find a
metal which was not readily wetted by water and which
had an affinity for greasy ink. This would be made the image
area on the plate, whilst a second metal easily wetted by water
would be made the non-image. Copper is very *hydrophobic* or
"water hating" and was an obvious choice for the image area.

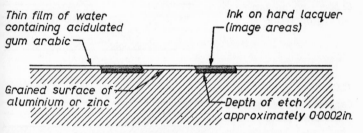

FIG. 15.1. A "DEEP ETCH" LITHO PLATE

On the other hand, aluminium and chromium are both
hydrophilic or "water loving" and are suitable for the non-
image. Fig. 15.2 (*a*) shows one type of bimetallic plate using
copper and chromium.

Fig. 15.2 (*b*) shows a trimetallic plate with a steel base
plated with copper and then with chromium.

In both cases the copper image is bared by etching down
through the thin layer of chromium.

This affinity of copper for ink is made use of in other ways
in the industry. The durability and affinity for ink of a deep-
etch image can be improved by the application of a thin layer
of copper and in the same way steel ink rollers can be made
more ink-receptive.

Copper resists most forms of corrosion as do its alloys which
include the brasses (copper-zinc), the bronzes (copper-tin), and
phosphor-bronzes (copper, tin, and phosphorus). It is unaffected by dry or moist air providing it is free from carbon

dioxide and acid vapours. A green coating of copper salts eventually forms when these are present. Concentrated sulphuric acid and concentrated hydrochloric acid have little effect on copper but it is attacked by nitric acid. Ferric chloride $FeCl_3$ or iron perchloride as it is still called in the trade, is the solution used to etch copper. Ferric chloride is a salt and is strongly hydrolysed in aqueous solution. Hydrolysis

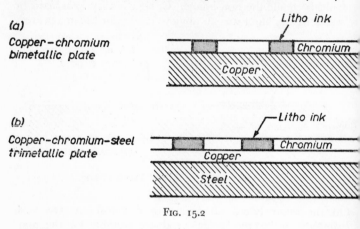

(a)

Copper–chromium bimetallic plate

(b)

Copper–chromium–steel trimetallic plate

FIG. 15.2

is the process in which water breaks up a salt into an acid and a base.

$$FeCl_3 + 3H_2O \rightleftharpoons Fe(OH)_3 + 3HCl$$

Ferric   Hydrochloric
hydroxide   acid

Since hydrochloric acid is a strong acid and ferric hydroxide only a weak base, solutions of ferric chloride are strongly acidic. The solutions used to etch gravure plates all appear to have pH's below zero. One advantage of ferric chloride as an etchant for copper is that no gas is produced in the reaction. If gas is produced small bubbles held on the surface of a metal, perhaps in the cells of a gravure plate would locally prevent contact between the etchant and the metal and so slow down the rate of etch in that area.

The reaction between copper and ferric chloride is thought to be as follows—

$$\underset{\text{copper}}{Cu} + \underset{\text{ferric chloride}}{2FeCl_3} = \underset{\text{cupric chloride}}{CuCl_2} + \underset{\text{ferrous chloride}}{2FeCl_2}$$

Ferric chloride, an *oxidizing agent*, has *oxidized* the copper to cupric chloride and in doing so has itself been *reduced* to ferrous chloride (Chapter 10).

$$\underset{\text{Copper}}{Cu} \xrightarrow[\text{loss of 2 electrons}]{} \underset{\text{Cupric ion}}{Cu^{++}}$$
$$= \text{OXIDATION}$$

$$\underset{\text{Ferric ion}}{Fe^{+++}} \xrightarrow[\text{gain of 1 electron}]{} Fe^{++}$$
$$= \text{REDUCTION}$$

Notice that the hydrochloric acid formed by hydrolysis appears to take no part in the reaction.

Experiment 1. The Etching of Copper

Prepare some small pieces of clean copper plate (about 3 cm × 1 cm). Mark an area of each plate with a wax crayon to form a resist. Just cover one of these plates with dilute nitric acid in a test tube. Remove, wash and examine the plate after about five minutes and record your observations. Repeat with the following solutions: Concentrated acetic acid, concentrated hydrochloric acid, ferric chloride solution (30 degrees Baumé), and a dilute solution of silver nitrate. Work out the equation for the reaction with silver nitrate.

Experiment 2. To Investigate the Effect of the Concentration of Ferric Chloride on the Rate of Etch on Bare Copper
(Group experiment)

(*a*) Cut eight 4 cm × 4 cm squares of copper from one plate. Give each piece some identification mark, clean, dry, and then weigh separately.

(*b*) Make up seven solutions of ferric chloride ranging from about 20 to 45 degrees Baumé (i.e. approx. 20 per cent to 60 per cent solutions). Measure 100 ml of each of these solutions into seven 250 ml beakers. Check that the temperature of each solution is the same.

(*c*) Measure 100 ml of concentrated hydrochloric acid into an eighth 250 ml beaker.

(*d*) Carefully lower one piece of copper into each of the eight beakers. Make certain that they are all placed in similar positions, preferably standing vertically against a glass stopper or similar inert material. After exactly ten minutes, remove the squares from the solutions, wash under the tap, dry, and re-weigh.

(e) Calculate the percentage loss in weight of the copper in each of the eight solutions. Draw a graph showing the relationship between the percentage loss in weight and the Baumé reading of the ferric chloride. From the graph make an estimate of the strength of the ferric chloride solution giving the maximum rate of etch in a still bath.

ZINC

Zinc is used for letterpress line blocks and litho plates. In this country copper is generally preferred for fine screen and colour half-tone blocks but on the Continent these too are often made from zinc.

At ordinary temperatures zinc is brittle and crystalline but between 120°C and 150°C it becomes pliable and can be rolled into sheets. When heated over 200°C it is actually more brittle than when it is cold. We have already seen that its low melting point and poor dimensional stability above 200°C make it a difficult metal to process. If you look at the surface of copper and zinc plates under a microscope, you will see that the zinc has a coarser crystalline structure. This is the main reason why copper is preferred for fine work, even though it is more expensive than zinc. In recent years special zincs have been developed to compete with the magnesium used for powderless etched letterpress blocks. These "micro-zincs" have a much finer crystalline structure than ordinary zinc and they will etch almost as quickly as magnesium.

Zinc has similar strength to aluminium but it is less elastic. If you suspend equal strips of aluminium and zinc plate and load them with equal weights, both metals will stretch, but when the weights are removed the aluminium recovers almost completely whilst the zinc does not. On long litho runs zinc plates (30 in. × 40 in.) have been shown to stretch $\frac{1}{8}$ in. to $\frac{1}{4}$ in. round the cylinder.

With only a small amount of water vapour present in the air there is only a very slight reaction between zinc and the oxygen. This reaction is greatly increased at higher humidities, and if a zinc litho plate is left with a film of water on it, it will oxidize much more rapidly than if it were dry. The layer of oxide which forms on the surface does protect the metal from further attack providing that the atmosphere is free of acid vapours. Unfortunately, an industrial atmosphere is not free from these vapours (over 5,000,000 tons of sulphur dioxide are discharged over Britain every year). Under these conditions zinc is steadily corroded. Zinc blocks and plates should be dried and stored in an air-conditioned room with a low relative humidity, or kept in a moisture-proof package.

The corrosion resistance of iron or steel is improved by a protective coating of zinc. This process, known as "galvanizing," usually consists of dipping the article in a bath of molten zinc, but alternatively the zinc can be electrodeposited.

Chemical Properties of Zinc. Zinc is attacked by dilute hydrochloric, sulphuric, and nitric acids. The purer the metal, the slower will be the reaction. Hydrogen gas is given off in the reactions with hydrochloric or sulphuric, but not with nitric. The course of the reaction with nitric acid depends on the strength of the acid. In etching zinc blocks the solution is usually about a 10 per cent solution of concentrated nitric acid in water and the products of this reaction are mainly zinc nitrate and nitric oxide gas

$$3Zn + 8HNO_3 = 3Zn(NO_3)_2 + 2NO + 4H_2O$$

If the solution is much weaker, no gas is evolved and ammonium nitrate and zinc nitrate are formed and if the acid is concentrated, then brown fumes of nitrogen peroxide gas are given off. The very slight etch made into a "deep-etch" litho plate may be made with a mixture of calcium chloride, ferric chloride, and hydrochloric acid. Both the ferric chloride and the hydrochloric acid attack the zinc—

$$Zn + 2FeCl_3 = ZnCl_2 + 2FeCl_2$$

$$Zn + 2HCl = ZnCl_2 + H_2$$

EXPERIMENT 3. THE ETCHING OF ZINC

Prepare some small pieces of clean zinc plate (about 3 cm × 1 cm). Place one of these pieces in a test tube and add sufficient dilute sulphuric acid to cover the metal. Try to identify the gas which is given off. Record your observations and try to write the equation for the reaction. Repeat this experiment with each of the following solutions—

Concentrated nitric acid (carry out in a fume cupboard).
10 per cent solution of conc. nitric acid.
1 per cent solution of conc. nitric acid (cover part of the zinc with an acid resist).
Dilute acetic acid.
Dilute hydrochloric acid.
Concentrated sodium hydroxide.
Dilute silver nitrate.

ALUMINIUM

Aluminium's most important application in the printing industry is as a metal for "surface" and "deep-etch" litho plates. It is also used for bimetal litho plates, letterpress blocks and in alloys for composing room furniture.

Although 100 years ago aluminium was a precious metal worth £7 an ounce, today the world output of the metal ranks next to that of iron and steel. This swift rise to importance is largely due to its remarkable properties. It has a very low specific gravity compared with most other metals (*see* Table 8) and, although pure aluminium is not particularly strong, its alloys have great strength. It is ductile, malleable (e.g. foil $\frac{1}{500}$ in. thick) fairly soft and weight for weight is a better conductor of electricity than copper.

Aluminium can be rolled into thin flexible sheets for litho plates and, since it is a lighter colour than zinc, it is easier to see an image on its surface. Both aluminium and zinc litho plates are grained to improve their capacity to hold water and to hold an image, a process which more than doubles the surface area of the plate. Of the two metals aluminium is capable of taking a finer grain than zinc. One of aluminium's outstanding advantages is its ability to protect itself against corrosion by the atmosphere. It is an active metal and a film of aluminium oxide quickly forms on its surface in air. Fortunately, although this oxide layer is thin, it is hard and well "keyed" on to the metal, and is able to protect the reactive aluminium underneath from further attack. Incidentally, it also makes the soldering of aluminium difficult.

This film of oxide can be thickened up to $\frac{1}{1000}$ in. by the process known as "anodizing." The metal is suspended in a bath containing either chromic or sulphuric acid solutions, and an electric current is passed as in electroplating. Oxygen is steadily released from the solution, reacts with the aluminium and builds up a layer of aluminium oxide on the surface. By varying the reaction conditions the oxide layer can be laid down either as a soft grey coating or as a hard bright transparent film. Litho plates with improved wear and corrosion resistance are produced from anodized aluminium.

We have already seen that whilst copper is hydrophobic aluminium is hydrophilic. The fact that aluminium has a greater affinity for water and thus a lower affinity for ink than zinc is important in litho. Other things being equal, aluminium will run cleaner than zinc or, to put it another way, aluminium can be run with less water than zinc. There is some evidence to suggest that it is the aluminium oxide that provides the hydrophilic surface for aluminium and if this is so then mechanical or chemical damage to the oxide layer should be avoided. It is known that chemical treatment of metals can change the affinity of the surface. For example, copper which is normally hydrophobic can be made hydrophilic with a particular chemical treatment.

Aluminium reacts readily with hydrochloric acid giving hydrogen, more slowly with sulphuric and only very slightly with nitric acid. The etching solution used in making "deep-etch" aluminium litho plates normally includes ferric chloride, cupric chloride, and hydrochloric acid.

MAGNESIUM

Magnesium has been called the lightweight champion of metals since it combines low specific gravity (1·74) with a relatively high strength. This strength may be doubled or even trebled when small amounts of other metals are blended with magnesium. The development of the jet aircraft was largely made possible by these magnesium alloys. In 1943 the world production of magnesium was 240,000 tons compared with 1,000 tons in 1920 and 20,000 tons in 1937. At the end of the war in 1945 new uses for magnesium were sought in an attempt to absorb the enormous quantities of magnesium which could be produced. The printing industry provided one of these new applications and today magnesium is commercially used for powderless etched letterpress blocks.

Magnesium is rather a brittle metal. It can be etched more rapidly than zinc since it is a more reactive metal, but for the same reason it is more subject to corrosion. Corrosion need not be a serious drawback to the use of either metal providing that careful precautions are taken in the storage and use of the blocks. Magnesium is attacked by dilute acids and by several salt solutions but unlike aluminium and zinc it is quite stable to alkalis.

At some time or other you have probably seen magnesium ribbon burning with a brilliant white flame or at least the effects of magnesium in a firework. It may seem odd that the same metal could be used to make printing plates and frying pans. The explanation is that magnesium will burn only when melted in contact with large supplies of air, so that the finely divided forms of the metal provide the greatest fire risk. Nitric acid forms the basis of etchants for magnesium, the main reaction being—

$$Mg + 2HNO_3 = Mg(NO_3)_2 + H_2$$

CHROMIUM AND NICKEL

These metals are important in two ways—

1. *In Alloys* (e.g. British "silver" coinage = 75 per cent copper + 25 per cent nickel, one type of stainless steel = 18 per cent chromium + 8 per cent nickel).

2. *As surface coatings on other metals.*

Their outstanding properties are those of corrosion resistance and hardness (Table 9). Chromium is somewhat harder than nickel and chromium plating is often put on top of a layer of nickel.

In the printing industry their function is to improve the wear and corrosion resistance of printing surfaces. They are electroplated on to stereos, electros, bimetallic litho plates, and gravure plates and cylinders.

EXERCISES

1. List the chief uses in the printing industry of the following metals: copper, zinc, aluminium, magnesium, chromium, nickel. Mention the properties which make the metals particularly suitable for the uses to which you have referred.   (FTC/1960.)

2. Give an account of the probable reactions which take place in etching: (a) zinc in nitric acid solution, and (b) copper in ferric chloride solution.
(Photo/1959/Int.)

3. Compare the properties of aluminium and zinc in relation to their uses in lithography.

4. Compare the characteristics of the metals zinc, copper, aluminium, and magnesium with special reference to: (a) surface oxidation and corrosion; (b) physical change at high temperatures; (c) hardness; (d) etching in relief with special reference to the type of solution preferred for the purpose.   (Photo/1959/Fin.)

5. Describe the probable chemical reaction in each of the following cases in which the metal is completely immersed in the solution: (a) copper in aqueous nitric acid; (b) copper in ferric chloride solution; (c) zinc in aqueous nitric acid; (d) magnesium in aqueous nitric acid.
(Photo/1961/Fin.)

6. Compare the properties of zinc and magnesium in relation to their uses in photo-engraving.

CHAPTER 16

CHEMISTRY OF PHOTOGRAPHY

MOST of us have pressed the shutter of a camera to take a photograph at some time or other. In what is usually a fraction of a second, we let sufficient light into the camera to produce later a permanent image on the film. For this to be possible, the film must carry an even coating of an extremely light-sensitive material, i.e. a material which changes either

FIG. 16.1

physically or chemically when exposed to light. A great many materials have this property of change under the action of light, although it is not always an advantage. Most of the pigments and dyes which colour printing inks, paints, and textiles fade when exposed.

Turn back the lapel of an old coat and compare the part that it covered with the cloth below the lapel. You may find that the dyed cloth has taken a photograph of the shape of the lapel (Fig. 16.1).

This photograph may have taken years to produce, but the principle by which it formed is the same as it is for the picture taken in a fraction of a second in a camera.

The light-sensitive materials which are used in photography

are certain salts of the metal silver, *silver chloride, silver bromide,* and *silver iodide*. These salts are outstandingly suitable because they are not strongly coloured, yet when exposed to only a small amount of light they begin to break down to give a finely divided form of silver which is black.

The Halogen Family. The four elements fluorine, chlorine, bromine, and iodine are members of a family which we called the HALOGENS. In many of their properties they resemble one another and any difference tends to be stepped down the group (Table 13).

Table 13

	Symbol	Atomic weight	Appearance	Boiling point	Solubility in water
Fluorine	F	19·00	pale yellow gas	−188°C	decomposes it instantly
Chlorine	Cl	35·46	dark greenish yellow gas	−35°C	slightly soluble
Bromine	Br	79·92	reddish brown liquid	63°C	very slightly soluble
Iodine	I	126·91	dark violet solid	184°C	almost insoluble

The Halides. All the halogens form compounds with metals and these are called the fluorides, chlorides, bromides, or iodides. The general name for all these salts is the HALIDES. In this very large class of compounds we have some familiar substances including: sodium chloride (common salt), ferric (iron) chloride (used for etching copper printing surfaces), potassium bromide (used as a restrainer in developing baths).

The Silver Halides. The light-sensitive salts for photography are three of the four SILVER HALIDES, silver chloride, silver bromide, and silver iodide. The fourth salt, silver fluoride, is not used since it is too soluble in water. The insoluble chloride, bromide, and iodide have similar properties and like the halogens the differences are stepped evenly in the order chloride, bromide, iodide. This is shown in Table 14.

Table 14

Silver chloride	AgCl	white	
Silver bromide	AgBr	pale yellow	increasing solubility ↑
Silver iodide	AgI	lemon yellow	

Making Silver Halides. These salts can be made simply by mixing silver with a particular halogen. This was actually

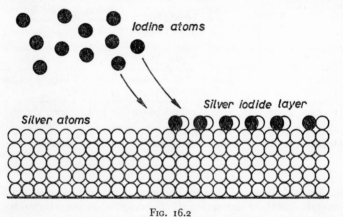

Fig. 16.2

the method used by Daguerre in the very early days of photography. He treated a silver plate with iodine vapour and so obtained a layer of light-sensitive silver iodide on its surface (Fig. 16.2).

$$Ag \ + \ I \ \rightarrow \ AgI$$
Silver   Iodine   Silver Iodide

If you ever get a chance, go to the photographic section of the Science Museum in London and have a look at the equipment actually used by Daguerre.

This direct method of making silver halides is not used in photography, since there is a much more convenient method. In this you mix two solutions, one containing a soluble silver salt and the other a soluble halide. A silver halide forms, and being almost insoluble in water it is thrown out of solution in a solid mass. The soluble silver salt used is always silver nitrate

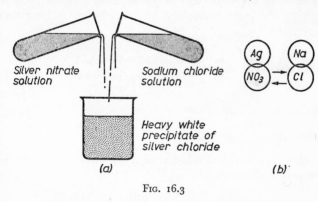

Silver nitrate solution

Sodium chloride solution

Heavy white precipitate of silver chloride

(a)

(b)

FIG. 16.3

and the soluble halide may be the sodium, potassium or ammonium salt.

EXPERIMENT 1. TO PREPARE SILVER CHLORIDE

Take one or two crystals of silver nitrate and dissolve them in a small amount of distilled water in a test tube. In a second test tube make up a similar solution of sodium chloride. The two solutions will look no different from water, but on mixing them an immediate white precipitate of silver chloride comes out of the solution (Fig. 16.3 (a)).

The equation for the reaction is—

$$AgNO_3 \ + \ NaCl \ = \ AgCl \ + \ NaNO_3$$

(soluble)   (soluble)   (white insoluble and light sensitive)   (soluble)

Notice how the metals silver and sodium have just exchanged their partners (Fig. 16.3 (b)).

This type of reaction is called "double decomposition" (Chapter 10).

As soon as the silver chloride has formed, filter it off and scrape some of the white solid over a piece of filter paper. Cover part of it with some opaque object of well-defined shape (a key or coin would be suitable) and leave in a light place. After 15 minutes or so, examine the exposed and unexposed parts. Some darkening will already have taken place in the exposed areas (Fig. 16.4).

The other silver halides can be made in a similar way by choosing the appropriate halide. A solution of potassium

FIG. 16.4

bromide mixed with a solution of silver nitrate will give the pale yellow silver bromide.

$$AgNO_3 + KBr = AgBr + KNO_3$$

Silver iodide can be prepared from potassium iodide and silver nitrate.

$$AgNO_3 + KI = AgI + KNO_3$$

When prepared in this way the particles of silver halide quickly group themselves into large lumps (coagulate) and drop to the bottom of the test tube.

These particles are much too coarse for a photographic surface. Furthermore, it would be very difficult to get an even coating on to a base material. We need to devise a method of preparing a silver halide in the form of small particles which can be suspended evenly in a solution. The answer to this problem and several others in photography is provided by a remarkable natural material—gelatin.

Gelatin. Gelatin is one of the proteins, substances with large complicated molecules containing carbon, nitrogen, and oxygen.

It is obtained from the bones, hide, sinew, and cartilage of animals, usually cattle, by treatment with hot water for a long period. Gelatin does not occur as such in these materials but is formed in the reaction with water (hydrolysis) and passes into solution. If this solution is separated and allowed to cool, it sets to a jelly or "gel" if more than 2 per cent of gelatin is present (this percentage varies with the grade of the

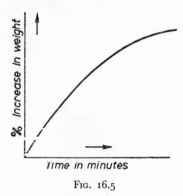

FIG. 16.5

gelatin). This jelly is shredded, washed, refined, and finally concentrated. Gelatin is supplied in the form of flakes, beads, powder, or brittle sheets.

The Properties of Gelatin

1. Gelatin does not dissolve in cold water, although it swells and will absorb many times its own weight of water.

EXPERIMENT 2. TO INVESTIGATE THE SWELLING PROPERTIES AND SOLUBILITY OF GELATIN IN WATER

Take a piece of sheet gelatin, about two inches square, and weigh it on a laboratory balance. Place it in a beaker of cold water, leave for 3 minutes, then take out the gelatin, remove the surface moisture and reweigh. Work out the percentage increase in weight. Repeat this process of soaking and weighing for periods of 3–5 minutes until the gelatin cannot be conveniently handled. Draw a graph showing how the percentage increase in weight varies with time (Fig. 16.5).

Finally, carefully warm the swollen gelatin in water and record the temperature when it begins to dissolve.

2. Gelatin dissolves easily in warm water forming a *colloidal* solution (*see* below). When this solution is allowed to cool then a gel forms, if 2 per cent of gelatin is present.

3. Gelatin forms a tough film with good adhesion to most surfaces (woodworkers' glue is a crude form of gelatin).

4. Gelatin contains small quantities of impurities, e.g. thiocarbamides, which increase the sensitivity of gelatin photographic emulsions.

5. Gelatin can be hardened by such chemicals as alum to reduce its tendency to swell in water and to increase the temperature at which it dissolves in water.

Fig. 16.6

We shall see later that every one of these properties is made use of in the photographic application of gelatin.

Colloidal Solutions. A colloidal solution, like that of gelatin, differs from a true molecular solution, mainly in the size of the particles mixed with the solvent. Although the colloidal particles are much larger than the single molecules or ions which exist in a true solution, they are still too small to be seen under an ordinary microscope. Since they all carry the same electrical charge, all positive or all negative, they repel one another and are prevented from coagulating into large particles which would settle out (Fig. 16.6).

A Photographic Emulsion. In making silver bromide we mixed a solution of silver nitrate with a solution of potassium bromide. Yellow silver bromide formed immediately and settled out of the solution in large particles. If we make up a solution of gelatin and add this to one of the two solutions before mixing, the silver bromide forms in the presence of gelatin. The colloidal particles of gelatin act as carriers for the

silver halide and hold it suspended in the solution in the form
of tiny particles (Fig. 16.7).

EXPERIMENT 3. TO PREPARE A SIMPLE PHOTOGRAPHIC EMULSION

Take 2 gm of gelatin and add to 20 c.c. of distilled water. Leave to soak
for as long as possible, then warm gently until all the gelatin passes into
solution. Dissolve about 0·5 gm of sodium chloride in 20 c.c. of water,

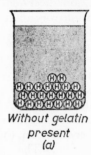

Silver bromide prepared

*Without gelatin
present
(a)*

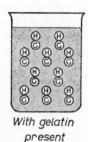

$\bigoplus$= *Halide
particles*

$\copyright$= *Gelatin
particles*

*With gelatin
present
(b)*

FIG. 16.7. A PHOTOGRAPHIC EMULSION BASICALLY CONSISTS OF THE
SUSPENSION OF MINUTE PARTICLES OF A SILVER HALIDE IN GELATIN

warm and add to the gelatin solution, adjusting the temperature of the
mixed solution to between 70°C and 90°C. Dissolve about 1 gm of silver
nitrate in 5 c.c. of distilled water by warming, and add this solution slowly
to the gelatin-chloride mixture. The mixture is now light-sensitive and if
possible should be kept in the dark or in a red light. When the solution is at
a suitable consistency, run a thin covering of the emulsion over a clean glass
plate. Leave to set in a dark room, and when the coating is dry, cover with
a simple negative or some form of stencil and expose to light. This can be
done most quickly by exposing through the back of the plate under an

ultra-violet lamp, or some other suitable light source. In this way you will have produced a surface on which you can take a photograph. This particular emulsion, made in the presence of excess silver nitrate, will darken without being developed but it must be fixed for the image to be permanent (*see* fixing).

The Speed of an Emulsion. Silver chloride, silver bromide, and silver iodide vary in their sensitivity to light. Emulsions often contain a mixture of two of these salts. By varying the proportions of each used it is possible to vary the speed of the emulsion.

Silver bromide forms the basis of most emulsions on film or glass, with or without small amounts of the iodide present. Less sensitive chloride or chloride/bromide emulsions are often coated on to paper supports.

Particle size is another factor which affects the film speed. The coarser the grain, the more sensitive is the halide and the faster the film. The grain size depends on the reaction conditions in the preparation of the emulsion, e.g. temperature, speed of mixing. It may also be increased after the emulsion has been prepared in a "ripening" process, in which the emulsion is heat treated at about 55°C for 30 to 60 minutes.

The Base Material. The photographic suspension is coated on to glass, paper, or film. Film base was formerly celluloid (cellulose nitrate + camphor), but today it is one of the non-inflammable plastics, cellulose acetate, polystyrene, or a polyester.

Exposure to Light. We must now consider what happens when our coating of halide grains in gelatin is exposed to light (Fig. 16.8).

The silver halides are unstable to light, breaking down into metallic silver and the free halogen, e.g.

Silver bromide breaks down to silver and bromine—

$$AgBr \xrightarrow{\text{light}} Ag + Br$$

Fortunately the metallic silver is not in the white lustrous form that we are familiar with, but in a finely divided form which is black.

If they were allowed to, the silver and bromine would recombine in the dark to give silver bromide again—

$$Ag + Br \xrightarrow{\text{dark}} AgBr$$

However another advantage of gelatin is that it is able to absorb small quantities of free halogen. In our example, it

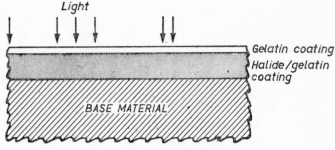

FIG. 16.8

would absorb the chlorine, so that the reaction giving metallic silver is unable to reverse later in the dark.

On exposing a film only a very small amount of the halide breaks down to black silver, under the action of light. In fact there is no visible difference between an exposed and un-exposed film. Even so, the quantity of silver formed is proportional to the amount of light falling on a particular part of the film.

Development. Exposure and development are very closely related for the reaction which starts in the camera is completed in the developing bath. It has been calculated that for every atom of silver freed in the camera, 1,000,000,000 are formed in developing. The action of light on certain halide grains allows the chemicals in the developing bath to convert these particular grains into black silver. Exposure is to development as a detonator is to a bomb. The second stage gives much the greater effect, but it is not possible without the first.

The main ingredient in a developing bath is the reducing agent. Reduction and reducing agents are discussed in

Chapter 10. In this particular example, a silver halide is reduced to metallic silver, e.g.

$$AgBr \rightarrow Ag + Br$$

(the reducing agent supplies an electron to a silver ion Ag^+ in the AgBr and converts it to Ag).

$$Ag^+ \rightarrow Ag \atop Black$$

There are hundreds of reducing agents which will convert a silver halide into silver but only a few of these selectively convert the light-struck halide grains.

Those that are suitable are usually derivatives of benzene C_6H_6. The structural formula of benzene is—

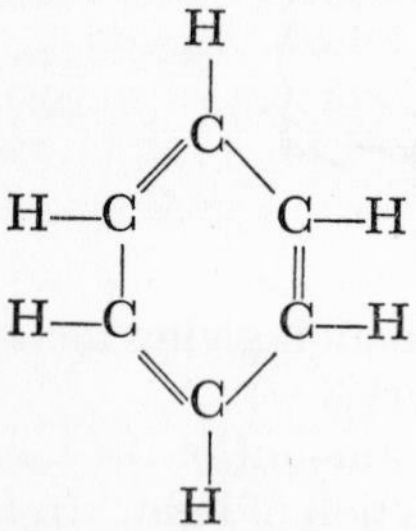

H
|
C

H—C   C—H

H—C   C—H

C
|
H

or as it is usually written in short—

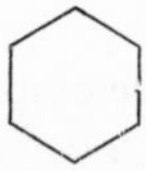

Some examples of commonly used reducing agents in developers are—

Hydroquinone

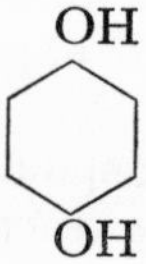

OH

OH

Metol

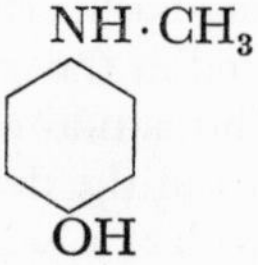

$NH \cdot CH_3$

OH

Para-aminophenol

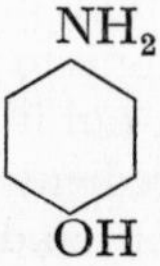

NH_2

OH

OTHER INGREDIENTS IN THE DEVELOPING SOLUTION

The Accelerator. The reducing agents used in developing are only active in alkaline solution. The alkali used is normally either: sodium hydroxide NaOH (caustic soda), or sodium carbonate $Na_2CO_3 \cdot 10 H_2O$ (washing soda). A secondary effect of this alkali is to increase the swelling of the gelatin which is at a minimum at the iso-electric point (pH 4·8).

The Restrainer. One of the products of the developing reaction is potassium bromide KBr. In any chemical reaction, as the concentration of the products increases the rate of reaction is slowed up. If, therefore, we have some potassium bromide in our developer at the start, we can be certain that the reaction will not be too fast to be controlled.

The Preservative. There is always a tendency for oxygen in the air to oxidize the developing agent. Sodium sulphite is usually added to prevent this oxidation and thus to keep the solution clear.

EXPERIMENT 4. TO INVESTIGATE THE ACTION OF A DEVELOPER

Mix small quantities of solutions of potassium iodide and silver nitrate. Spread some of the yellow silver iodide formed on to a filter paper and leave this exposed to the light for a few moments. Dissolve a few grains of hydroquinone and sodium carbonate in a small volume of distilled water in a test tube, and spot this on to the exposed silver iodide. Immediately the area affected will turn black.

Fixing the Image. Those areas which have not been reduced to metallic silver, still carry a coating of unexposed silver halide. This coating remains light-sensitive and if left would slowly darken and fog the whole photograph. The process of removing these unexposed silver halides is called fixing. Since the silver salts are almost completely insoluble in water, it is necessary to use a special chemical to dissolve them out of the coating. This chemical is—

Sodium thiosulphate $Na_2S_2O_3$ ("hypo")

If you try dissolving a very small quantity of silver chloride (prepared as in earlier experiments) in cold water then add a few grains of hypo to the water you will see the hypo dissolve and the silver chloride pass into solution.

The reactions are probably as follows—

$$AgCl + Na_2S_2O_3 = Na(AgS_2O_3) + NaCl$$

insoluble   soluble   slightly soluble   soluble

$$AgCl + 2Na_2S_2O_3 = Na_3Ag(S_2O_3)_2 + NaCl$$

insoluble   soluble   soluble   soluble

Other Ingredients in the Fixing Bath. There is a tendency for developing solution to be brought over into the fixing bath, thus allowing development to continue unless it is checked. One answer to this is to rinse the photograph in a bath of water or weak acid between developing and fixing. However, it is more normal to use an acid fixing bath. Acidic conditions effectively stop development, since the reducing agent is more active in alkaline solution. Unfortunately, hypo is not stable in acid conditions, e.g.

$$Na_2S_2O_3 + 2HCl \rightarrow H_2SO_3 + \underline{\underline{S}} + 2NaCl$$

Sulphur is formed giving a cloudy bath.

This reaction can be reversed by the presence of a high concentration of sulphite ions. These sulphite ions together with acidic conditions are usually provided by: (a) sodium metabisulphite $Na_2S_2O_5$ or by (b) sodium sulphite + acetic acid.

A fixing bath may also contain a "hardener" which reduces the swelling of gelatin in further processing.

The hardener may be: potash alum—

$$K_2SO_4 \cdot Al_2(SO_4)_3 \cdot 24H_2O$$

or chrome alum—

$$K_2SO_4 \cdot Cr_2(SO_4)_3 \cdot 24H_2O$$

THINGS TO LEARN

1. A photographic emulsion mainly consists of a dispersion of tiny grains of a light-sensitive silver salt in gelatin.

2. The functions of the gelatin are: (a) to provide a means of getting the silver salt in a fine form, suspended in a solution;

(b) to protect the halide grains from mechanical damage; (c) to protect the grains from excessive exposure to light; (d) to provide impurities which improve the efficiency of the emulsion; (e) to provide good adhesion for the coating on the base material.

3. Under the action of light, silver halides break down into black metallic silver and the halogen, e.g.

$$AgBr \rightarrow Ag + Br$$

4. In photography, this reaction is only triggered by the light in the camera and completed in the developing bath.

5. The ingredients in a developing bath are a reducing agent, an alkaline accelerator, a preservative, and a restrainer.

6. Fixing is a process in which the unexposed silver halides are removed. The main ingredient in the bath is sodium thiosulphate (hypo).

OTHER BOOKS TO READ

SOUTHWORTH AND BENTLEY, *Photographic Chemicals and Chemistry* (Pitman)
K. M. HORNSBY, *Basic Photographic Chemistry* (Fountain)
H. BAINES, *The Science of Photography* (Fountain)
P. GLAFKIDES, *Photographic Chemistry* (Fountain)
H. M. CARTWRIGHT, *Graphic Arts Manual* (Ilford)

EXERCISES

1. Write the equation for the preparation of a silver halide used in photography. Discuss fully the meaning of the equation and describe the visible changes which take place when the reaction is carried out.

2. What is meant by the statement that "gelatin is a typical colloid"?
(Photo/1960/Fin.)

3. Explain the function of: (a) gelatin; and (b) the silver halide in a photographic emulsion.

4. Outline the properties of gelatin and explain which of these properties are made use of in its photographic application and which of them act as a disadvantage.

5. (a) Describe the function of gelatin in a photographic emulsion. (b) Name two silver halides often used in a photographic emulsion and give a brief account of their properties.   (Photo/1960/Fin.)

6. Discuss the reaction which takes place on exposing and developing a photographic emulsion. Why is it necessary to fix the image formed?

7. What is the function of a developing solution? Outline the main ingredients of such a solution explaining the purpose of each.

CHAPTER 17

IMAGES ON METAL

In the production of a printing plate or block for each of the major printing processes there is the important step of converting an image on film or glass into an image on metal. This is usually done by making use of the change in solubility of a light-sensitive coating on exposure to light. If this light-sensitive coating on metal is exposed through a negative or positive, it is hardened and made less soluble in proportion to the amount of light falling on a particular area. The soluble areas can now be dissolved away (developed) and the metal selectively etched (Chapter 15) with the hardened coating acting as a resist. Although there are many differences in practical detail for each process, this is basically the method by which the image on a printing plate for letterpress, litho, and gravure is produced from a photographic image.

The coating usually consists of a colloid together with a salt, ammonium or potassium dichromate, making the mixture light-sensitive. In the trade these dichromates are often wrongly called bichromates. We saw in an earlier chapter that colloids form solutions which differ from ordinary molecular solutions mainly in their larger particle size, e.g. the particles in a solution of starch are many times larger than those in a salt solution. The colloids which are important in printing images on to metal are gum arabic, egg albumen, gelatin, and fish glue, although a number of others including shellac, horse blood plasma ("Patracoat"), modified forms of casein, and polyvinyl alcohol are also in common use.

Gum Arabic is obtained from certain varieties of the acacia tree found in the Middle East. It is collected from the trees, separated from the bark, dried, graded, and supplied in the form of yellowish brown lumps. In its natural state it is thought to be a mixture of arabic acid with its calcium, potassium and magnesium salts. It dissolves slowly in water to form a gummy colloidal solution. Gum arabic sensitized with ammonium dichromate is the coating used in producing a "deep-etch" litho plate.

Egg Albumen is a protein obtained from white of egg. It may be supplied in the form of bright yellow flakes or as a powder. It dissolves in water to form a colloidal solution, which can be coagulated by heat, alcohol, and by some salts. Coagulation means the precipitation or suspension of a substance from a solution in an insoluble form. Like all these natural colloids, its solutions are subject to bacterial attack and mould growth, but preservatives can be added to increase their stability. Albumen with ammonium dichromate is used in the production of letterpress line blocks and surface litho plates.

Gelatin (Chapter 16) sensitized with potassium dichromate is used in the production of plates and cylinders for gravure. The way in which it is used is different from other processes where a dichromated colloidal solution is coated direct on to the metal, dried, exposed, and developed. Carbon tissue consists of a coating of pigmented gelatin on a thin paper backing. This is sensitized by immersion in a dilute solution of potassium dichromate, squeegeed on to plate glass, dried, exposed through screen and positive, and developed, before being transferred to the copper plate.

Fish Glue or gelatose is a degraded form of gelatin obtained from fish skin and bones. If a solution of gelatin is overheated it breaks down into gelatose and the process can be taken a stage further to yield gelatone which has no practical value as a printing colloid. Gelatose mainly differs from gelatin in that it will never form a gel. It is supplied in the form of a thick colloidal solution which is mixed with ammonium dichromate and more water to form the coating solution. This dichromated fish glue is used to produce half-tone blocks for letterpress. The areas of coating affected by light are baked to form an effective acid resist.

Examine samples of the colloids gelatin, fish glue, gum arabic, and egg albumen. Make up solutions of each and observe the effects of heat, alcohol, salt solutions, etc., on these solutions.

Ammonium dichromate $(NH_4)_2Cr_2O_7$ forms orange red crystals which are fairly soluble in water. The salt is prepared by neutralizing chromic acid with ammonium hydroxide. Ammonium hydroxide added to a solution of ammonium dichromate converts it to the yellow ammonium chromate $(NH_4)_2CrO_4$. If ammonia gas NH_3 is allowed to evaporate from this chromate solution it changes back into ammonium dichromate.

Potassium dichromate $K_2Cr_2O_7$ has similar properties to the ammonium salt already described, although it is a good deal

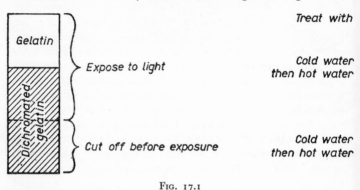

FIG. 17.1

less soluble. It is preferred to ammonium dichromate for sensitizing gelatin for gravure.

The Light-hardening Reaction. The nature of the reaction in which light changes the solubility of the dichromated colloid coating is not yet fully understood. The dichromates are oxidizing agents and the research that has been done on the reaction suggests that oxidation and reduction do take place. Light causes the dichromate to give up oxygen to oxidize the colloid and in doing so the dichromate is itself reduced.

EXPERIMENT 1. TO EXAMINE THE EFFECT OF LIGHT ON A
DICHROMATED COLLOID

(a) Take a strip of leaf gelatin about 3 in. by 1 in., and stand it upright in a 5 per cent solution of potassium dichromate at room temperature so that approximately two-thirds of the strip is immersed (Fig. 17.1). After five minutes remove the strip and examine. Notice that swelling has taken place and that the immersed portion is considerably thicker than the un-treated gelatin.

(b) Cut off a small piece of the dichromated gelatin and place in a beaker of cold water. Notice that the dichromate readily bleeds into the water. On warming the beaker, the gelatin and dichromate will pass into solution.

(c) Expose each side of the remainder of the original strip in sunlight or under an ultra-violet lamp for at least five minutes. After exposure, place the whole of the strip in cold water. Notice that the dichromate does not bleed out into the water in any quantity, suggesting that on the surface at least it is combined with the gelatin. It will also be seen that the undichromated parts swell much faster than those which are dichromated, and eventually this becomes the thicker portion.

(d) Finally place the strip in a beaker of hot water. The gelatin dissolves as expected but the exposed dichromated gelatin is unaffected.

Factors Affecting the Hardening Reaction. There are very many factors affecting the rate of hardening of the dichromated colloid. We will consider some of the more important of these.

1. The greater *the amount of light* falling on the coating the more hardening will take place. In turn this will depend on several other variables including the time of exposure, the nature of the positive or negative, the intensity of illumination, etc.

2. The reaction rate also depends on *the wavelength of the light*. The coatings are most sensitive to ultra-violet light and to the shorter wavelengths at the violet end of the visible spectrum. Wavelengths greater than 600 mμ have little or no effect on the coating and thus safe lights are usually yellow or red.

3. Hardening proceeds more quickly as *the temperature* is raised. Storage problems are created for the process worker by the fact that dichromated colloids harden slowly in the dark, but this "dark reaction" can be almost stopped by storing the sensitized material under refrigerated conditions.

4. If *the relative humidity* increases so does *the moisture content of the coating* and the hardening reaction proceeds more quickly.

5. As *the ratio of dichromate to colloid* is increased, the mixture

becomes more light-sensitive, but at the same time its storage life is reduced.

6. The higher *the pH of the coating*, i.e. the more alkaline, the lower is its sensitivity.

7. The greater *the thickness of the coating* the less sensitive it is to light. In turn, the thickness depends on many other variables including the density and viscosity of the coating solution, the whirler speed, the temperature of the plate and of the solution, and the relative humidity.

Other Light-sensitive Coatings. We have already seen that dichromated colloids have their drawbacks, notably the "dark reaction" and the need for close control of humidity and temperature in their use. With the exception of polyvinyl alcohol, the colloids are all natural materials difficult to control since one batch is never precisely the same as another. These are the main reasons why efforts have been made to find new materials to replace dichromated colloids. Presensitized litho plates based on diazo compounds and containing no dichromates or natural colloids are already commercially important.

THINGS TO LEARN

1. When a coating of a dichromated colloid, e.g. egg albumen + ammonium dichromate, is exposed to light, it is hardened and made less soluble in water. This reaction is made use of in transferring photographic images on film or glass to metal.

2. The speed of this reaction is influenced by a number of factors including the amount of light, the wavelength of this light, the temperature, the relative humidity, the moisture content of the coating, the ratio of dichromate to colloid, the pH of the coating and the thickness of the coating.

OTHER BOOKS TO READ

PAUL J. HARTSUCH, *Chemistry of Lithography* (Lithographic Technical Foundation, New York)

CARTWRIGHT and MACKAY, *Rotogravure* (Mackay Publishing Corp., U.S.A.)

SMITH, TURNER, and HALLAM, *Photo-engraving in Relief* (Pitman)

"Lithography in 1960," *Proceedings of the PATRA Offset-litho Conference* (PATRA)

H. M. CARTWRIGHT, *Graphic Arts Manual* (Ilford)

JORGENSEN AND BRUNO, *The Sensitivity of Bichromated Coatings used in Litho-graphy* (Lithographic Technical Foundation, New York)

EXERCISES

1. Discuss in general terms how dichromated colloids are made use of in converting an image on film or glass into an image on metal.

2. Describe briefly the more obvious characteristics and significance in graphic reproduction of: (a) gelatin; (b) process glue; (c) albumen; (d) shellac; (e) polyvinyl alcohol.   (Photo/1959/Fin.)

3. Write a brief account of the properties of gelatin with special reference to: (a) absorption of aqueous solutions; (b) melting and setting temperatures; (c) isoelectric point; and (d) reaction with alkali di-chromates in the dark and light.   (Photo/1961/Fin.)

4. Discuss some of the more important factors influencing the light-hardening of dichromated colloids.

CHAPTER 18

ELECTRICITY HELPS AND HINDERS

In a printing works electricity provides the power to run machines, light for photomechanical reproduction, heat for melting metal or drying some printing inks, and current for building up the surfaces of printing plates. Yet in the form known as static electricity it is one of the most persistent nuisances in machine operation, upsetting feed and delivery and sometimes even causing fires on high-speed machines which use inks based on inflammable solvents.

STATIC ELECTRICITY

About 2,000 years ago, a Greek philosopher named Thales discovered that a piece of amber rubbed with cloth was able to attract small bits of other materials. From the Greek word for amber, *elektron*, came our modern word electricity.

Thales' experiment can be repeated with a fountain pen, warmed and dried in front of a fire, and then rubbed on a coat sleeve. After rubbing, the pen will pick up small pieces of paper, dust and so on, or make the fine hair on the arm stand on end when it is brought near.

When two materials are rubbed together some electrons are transferred from one to the other. As electrons are negative electrical charges (Chapter 3) the material getting more than its fair share becomes negatively charged, while the one which loses electrons becomes positively charged. Which of the two becomes positive and which negative depends on the combination of materials used. Paper will be negatively charged if rubbed with silk or flannel but positively charged if rubbed on metal.

Friction is not the only cause of materials becoming charged. This may result from rapid separation, sudden change in pressure, heat or chemical action. A material retains its charges until they find a path by which they can escape to earth or until they are neutralized by an equal number of charges of opposite sign.

There is one rule about these charges which every printer should know—

Electric charges of the same sign repel each other but those of opposite sign attract each other.

The first part of the rule can be illustrated by rubbing two strips of dry paper with silk or flannel and hanging them very closely side by side. The lower ends of the strips will be held

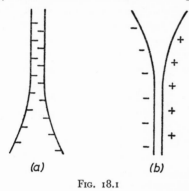

(a)   (b)

FIG. 18.1

apart by the force of repulsion between the negative charges on them (Fig. 18.1 (*a*)). If, however, a strip of negatively charged paper is suspended near one charged positively by rubbing it on metal, then the charges will attract each other and the two strips will stick together (Fig. 18.1 (*b*)). These represent two of the possible situations which may arise when paper or plastic sheets are being printed. Sheets may stick together because they become charged in opposite ways, or they may refuse to lie flat on each other because they have the same kind of charge.

A third possibility arises if one sheet is charged and another uncharged. Then a process known as *induction* takes place. The charges on the first sheet attract charges of opposite sign to the nearer side of the neutral sheet and repel those of similar sign to the far side of the sheet (Fig. 18.2 (*a*)). The

force of attraction or repulsion between two charges decreases
rapidly with increasing distance between them, so now the force
of attraction between the charges on the two sheets are greater
than the forces of repulsion. Therefore the two sheets will stick

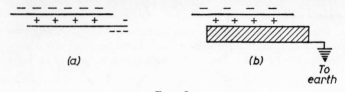

(a)   *(b)*
                                                    *To
                                                    earth*

FIG. 18.2

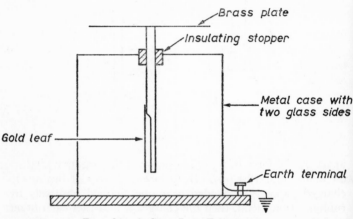

Fig. 18.3. A GOLD LEAF ELECTROSCOPE

together. Similarly any earthed part of the machine will attract
a charged sheet as a result of induction (Fig. 18.2 (*b*)), but in
this case the charges of like sign are driven away to earth where
they have as little effect on the total amount of electricity
present as a teaspoonful of water has on the level of the sea.

Identifying Static. To find out whether or not static
electricity is present, and also to discover the type of charge,
use is made of an instrument known as a *gold leaf electroscope*
(Fig. 18.3). This consists essentially of a gold leaf attached

at its upper end to a metal rod and lying loosely beside the flattened end of the rod. Alternatively two gold leaves may be used attached to the end of the rod and lying side by side.

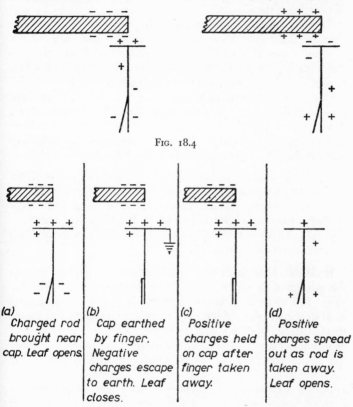

FIG. 18.4

(a) Charged rod brought near cap. Leaf opens.

(b) Cap earthed by finger. Negative charges escape to earth. Leaf closes.

(c) Positive charges held on cap after finger taken away.

(d) Positive charges spread out as rod is taken away. Leaf opens.

FIG. 18.5

When any charged object is brought near the metal plate on top of the instrument, charges of the same sign are driven down the rod to the leaf. The charges on rod and leaf repel each other causing the gold leaf to swing away from the rod (Fig. 18.4). As the object is withdrawn the charges redistribute themselves evenly and the leaf closes again. Some electroscopes have scales engraved on the glass sides for measuring the angle of deflection of the leaf, so obtaining an estimate of the amount of charge on the object.

To discover whether the object is positively or negatively charged the electroscope must first be charged itself by the process shown in Fig. 18.5. Note that a negatively charged rod is used to charge the electroscope positively and vice versa. If now a positively charged piece of paper is brought near the electroscope prepared as in Fig. 18.5 (d), then *more* positive charges will be driven down to the leaf, which will open wider. A neutral or negatively charged sheet will cause the leaf to close down. No charge should be regarded as definitely identified until it has satisfied one of the following conditions—

(i) A charge which causes the leaf of a positively charged electroscope to open wider is a positive charge;

(ii) A charge which causes the leaf of a negatively charged electroscope to open wider is a negative charge;

(iii) An object which causes the leaf to close in both cases is not charged at all.

Is Static Unavoidable? Static electricity is a trouble to the printer only when the material being printed is unable to act as a path to earth for charges which may be generated on it in one or more of the ways mentioned earlier. For paper this is rarely the case when the moisture content is 7 per cent or more, because there is then sufficient water present to allow the charges to flow off the paper through the frame of the machine to earth. If the machine has been mounted on anti-vibration supports it is useful to check that some metallic braided flex or other provision has been made for earthing the frame. When the moisture content of paper falls to 5 per cent or less, trouble from static is fairly certain to occur unless special steps are taken to prevent it.

The machine minder who hangs wet rags or blankets near his machine is raising the humidity of the surrounding air to a level which gives the paper enough moisture to allow the static charges to leak away. But, as we saw in Chapter 5, purely local changes in humidity may cause register or feeding difficulties, so such crude methods need to be replaced by effective air and paper conditioning, which are the best guarantee against static troubles.

Cellulose acetate, plastic, and similar films, however, are poor conductors of electricity under any circumstances, requiring other methods of dealing with the static problem.

Getting Rid of Static. To deal with situations in which relative humidity control is not enough to defeat static

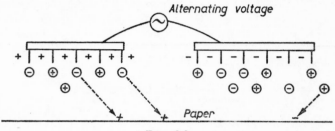

FIG. 18.6

electricity, various types of static eliminator are marketed for fitting to printing machines.

One type uses the principle of the lightning conductor to eliminate electrostatic charges—for lightning is only the discharge of the very large electrostatic charges which are generated on clouds. A rapidly alternating high voltage is applied to a row of needle points placed above the run of the paper. Under the influence of this voltage the air between the points and the paper becomes filled with positively and negatively charged particles (Fig. 18.6). The charges on the paper attract a particle of opposite sign to become neutralized.

A similar effect can be produced by hanging metallic tinsel or frayed-out flex from the frame of the machine (Fig. 18.7). Charges on the paper will induce charges of opposite sign on the metal points. These will charge particles of the surrounding air, which will then be attracted across the gap to neutralize those on the paper. This is the way a lightning conductor acts when a thunder cloud passes overhead.

The second type of eliminator is the anti-static spray which is applied to serve two purposes at the same time. It provides a conducting film over surfaces on which electrostatic charges are likely to accumulate and also acts as a lubricant to reduce the friction which might generate the charges.

A third type of eliminator uses a radioactive substance to ionize the air above the paper—that is, to divide some of the

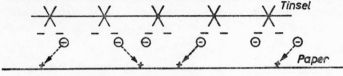

FIG. 18.7

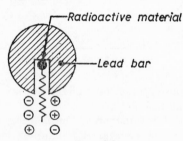

FIG. 18.8

molecules into positively and negatively charged particles. Because the radiation from these substances is harmful to living beings the substance is confined at the bottom of a narrow slot in a thick lead bar which shields the machine operator from the radiation (Fig. 18.8). Radiation from the slot ionizes the air and the charges on the paper are then neutralized in the same way as with a high-voltage bar.

ELECTRONS ON THE MOVE

So far we have mainly dealt with electrons more or less fixed on materials which do not conduct, or do not provide an easy path for, electricity. By using materials which are good conductors, such as metals, we can control the movement of electrons to provide an *electric current* and so make them work for us. A very much simplified picture is given in Fig. 18.9 (*a*), the large dots representing the fixed parts of the molecules and the small dots those electrons which are relatively free to move. When there is a voltage difference between the ends of the conductor the free electrons are attracted toward the end at the higher voltage—the positive end (Fig. 18.9 (*b*)). Eventually they will arrive at this end to flow out into the battery, transformer, or supply mains which must direct an

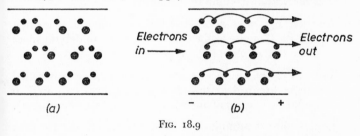

Fig. 18.9

equal number into the other end to maintain the electrical balance. Thus there is a steady movement of electrons along the conductor as long as the voltage difference remains the same. Note that this movement is in the opposite direction to that in which we normally say the current is flowing, that is, from positive to negative. The difficulty arises because the moving charges are negative, not positive as was assumed by the earlier investigators of electricity.

The freedom of movement of the electrons differs for different substances. Materials such as rubber, glass, and dry paper which allow hardly any movement at all are called *insulators*. The conductors differ from each other in their *resistance* to the passage of the current of electrons. The longer a conductor of a particular material is, the greater will be the resistance, and the thicker the conductor is the smaller will be the resistance. So the resistance of a piece of wire is given by the formula—

$$R = \frac{s \times L}{A}$$

where *s* is the *specific resistance* of the material (that is, the resistance of a cube with each side one centimetre in length), *L* is the length of the wire and *A* the area of cross-section. Resistance of wire is usually given in ohms (*see* below) per metre or per foot.

Ohm's Law. In general practice the units used for the measurement of electricity are—

OHM (Ω): the unit of resistance (defined as the resistance of a standard column of mercury);

AMPERE (A): often abbreviated to amp, the unit of current strength (defined as the current required to deposit silver at the rate of 0·001118 gm per second);

VOLT (V): the unit of electromotive force, popularly called voltage (defined as the electromotive force required to produce a current of one amp in a resistance of one ohm).

Long before these units had been established, the German scientist Ohm had discovered that—

The strength of the current in any conductor is proportional to the electromotive force acting at the ends and inversely proportional to the resistance of the conductor, provided that the temperature remains constant.

This is known as Ohm's law and may be written in the form of the equation—

$$I = \frac{E}{R} \qquad . \qquad . \qquad . \qquad . \quad (1)$$

where *I* is the current in amps, *E* is the electromotive force in volts, and *R* is the resistance in ohms. Indeed, the units were chosen to make this so.

While the equation is strictly true only for direct current (d.c.), in which the electrons always move in the same direction, it can be applied to alternating current (a.c.). Alternating current is obtained when the voltage difference is reversed periodically so that the electrons surge backward and forward like tiny pendulums. The voltage given for an a.c.

supply, as on a domestic meter, is an average value which gives the right answer when used in Ohm's law calculations. So a heating appliance with an effective resistance of 120 ohms connected to a 240 volt supply will take a current of 2 amps— that is 240 V divided by 120 Ω. Ohm's law can be used to

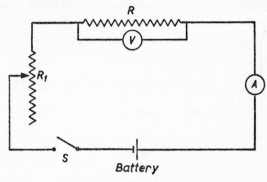

FIG. 18.10

calculate resistance or voltage as well as current, for eqn. (1) can also be written—

$$E = I \times R \qquad . \qquad . \qquad . \qquad (2)$$

or

$$R = \frac{E}{I} \qquad . \qquad . \qquad . \qquad (3)$$

Try working out for yourself what the voltage will be when a current of 3 amps flows in a conductor of resistance 8 ohms, and also the resistance of a wire which needs a 200-volt supply to make a current of 4 amps flow in it.*

EXPERIMENT 1. TO MEASURE AN UNKNOWN RESISTANCE BY APPLYING OHM'S LAW

Apparatus. Battery; switch; voltmeter; ammeter; fixed resistance; variable resistance; wire.

As shown in Fig. 18.10, the fixed resistance R is connected to a voltmeter V (for measuring the voltage between its ends), an ammeter A (to measure the strength of the current), the variable resistance R_1, a switch,

* The answers are 24 volts and 50 ohms.

and a battery. The connecting wires are represented by straight lines in the diagram. When the switch is closed the voltmeter will show the voltage across R and the ammeter the current passing through R. A series of different readings can be obtained on V and A by varying R_1. It will be found that the result of dividing each voltmeter reading by the corresponding ammeter reading will always give (within the limits of accuracy of the readings) the same figure, which will be the resistance in

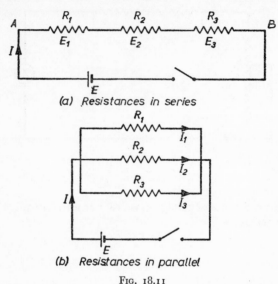

(a) Resistances in series

(b) Resistances in parallel

FIG. 18.11

ohms of R. A voltmeter is designed to take so small a current that its effect can be ignored compared with the much larger current in R.

Electrical appliances and resistances may be connected together in two ways known as *series* and *parallel*. In series they are connected as in Fig. 18.11 (*a*) so that the same current flows through all of them and the total voltage is shared between them. Parallel connexion is as in Fig. 18.11 (*b*), the current being shared between the resistances and the whole of the voltage acting on each one. Fairy lights on Christmas trees are connected in series, but electric lights in a house or on a motor-car are almost always connected in parallel.

If the total voltage between the points A and B in Fig. 18.11 (a) is E and the current in the circuit is I, then by Ohm's law we know that $E = I \times R$, where R is the total resistance between A and B. Similarly taking each resistance in turn—

$$E_1 = I \times R_1 \qquad E_2 = I \times R_2 \qquad E_3 = I \times R_3$$

$$\therefore \quad E = E_1 + E_2 + E_3 = I \times R_1 + I \times R_2 + I \times R_3$$

but E also equals $I \times R$

$$\therefore \qquad I \times R = I \times (R_1 + R_2 + R_3)$$

so, dividing each side by I,

$$R = R_1 + R_2 + R_3 \qquad . \qquad . \qquad . \quad (4)$$

From this it can be seen that the resulting resistance of any number of resistances in series is obtained by adding together the individual resistances. Supposing the resistances in Fig. 18.11 (a) were 5, 2, and 4 ohms respectively, then the total resistance would be 11 ohms.

A very different picture is seen in Fig. 18.11 (b). Here the main current I divides into three branches, so that—

$$I = I_1 + I_2 + I_3 \qquad . \qquad . \qquad . \quad (5)$$

The voltage E across all the resistances is the same, therefore

$$E = I_1 \times R_1 = I_2 \times R_2 = I_3 \times R_3 = I \times R$$

if R is used to denote the effective combined resistance. Thus—

$$I = \frac{E}{R} \qquad I_1 = \frac{E}{R_1} \qquad I_2 = \frac{E}{R_2} \quad \text{and} \quad I_3 = \frac{E}{R_3}$$

Substituting in (5), we have—

$$\frac{E}{R} = \frac{E}{R_1} + \frac{E}{R_2} + \frac{E}{R_3}$$

$$\therefore \qquad \frac{1}{R} = \frac{1}{R_1} + \frac{1}{R_2} + \frac{1}{R_3} \qquad . \qquad . \qquad . \quad (6)$$

So for resistances in parallel we find that the reciprocal of the combined resistance equals the sum of the reciprocals of the individual resistances. Taking the same values for the three resistances as we did for series connexion we have—

$$\frac{1}{R} = \frac{1}{5} + \frac{1}{2} + \frac{1}{4} = \frac{4 + 10 + 5}{20} = \frac{19}{20}$$

$$\therefore \qquad\qquad R = \frac{20}{19} = 1 \cdot 05 \text{ ohms}$$

Note that in parallel resistances the combined resistance is always smaller than the smallest of the single resistances.

Measuring Electric Power. When the local Electricity Board send in the bill for electricity used, the charge is based on a unit we have not yet discussed—the kilowatt (1,000 watts). The kilowatt is the unit used in practice to measure the power consumed in a circuit—the rate at which energy is expended in overcoming the resistance to the flow of the current. Remember that current is the rate of flow of electrical energy, while power is the rate of doing work or expending energy. The watt is defined as the power expended when a current of one ampere flows through a drop in electromotive force of one volt. There are 746 watts in one horsepower. The power used in any circuit is found, therefore, by multiplying voltage and current, so—

$$\text{watts} = \text{volts} \times \text{amps} \qquad \text{or} \qquad W = E \times I \quad . \quad (7)$$

But $$\qquad\qquad I = \frac{E}{R} \qquad \text{and} \qquad E = I \times R$$

$$\therefore \qquad\qquad\qquad W = \frac{E^2}{R} \qquad . \qquad . \qquad . \qquad . \quad (8)$$

or $$\qquad\qquad\qquad W = I^2 R \qquad . \qquad . \qquad . \qquad . \quad (9)$$

These three different ways of finding the power are used according to the facts we have about the circuit concerned. Suppose, for instance, we want to know what fuse should be used with a 3-kilowatt heater on a 240-volt supply. The size or "rating" of a fuse depends on the current it needs to carry. So we want to know the current, which can be found by substituting figures in eqn. (7) above—

$$3,000 \text{ watts} = 240 \text{ V} \times I$$

$$\therefore \qquad I = \frac{3,000}{240} = 12 \cdot 5 \text{ amps.}$$

So a 13-amp or 15-amp fuse will be needed. In a similar way the operating resistance and current consumption of an ordinary filament lamp can be found from its technical description. A 240-volt 120-watt lamp will need a current given by—

$$120 \text{ W} = 240 \text{ V} \times I$$

$$\therefore \qquad I = \frac{120}{240} = 0 \cdot 5 \text{ amps.}$$

To find the resistance we make use of eqn. (8)

$$120 \text{ W} = \frac{240 \times 240}{R}$$

$$\therefore \qquad R = \frac{240 \times 240}{120} = 480 \text{ ohms.}$$

From the current values in the examples above it will be clear that to leave the heater on all night uses twenty-five times the energy used by the lamp in the same time.

Sometimes factors other than resistance come into play in motors or electronic instruments using alternating current. In such cases these are combined into a single value called the *impedance* which is the equivalent of resistance and is measured in ohms.

Heat from Electricity. Most of the power expended when a current flows in a wire emerges in the form of heat or light. In fuses, which are made from metals of low melting point, this heat is sufficient to melt the wire (and so break the circuit) when the amount of current passing exceeds a set value

—5 amps, 10 amps, and so on. The light from a filament lamp is due to the wire being heated to a temperature of 2,000°C or more by the current passing through it. At such a high temperature it becomes white hot and glows brightly. As the heated wire would burn away very quickly if exposed to the oxygen of the atmosphere, it is enclosed in a glass envelope from which all the air has been removed and replaced by a gas which does not react with the hot metal. Electric fires and other heating appliances do not burn away mainly because they operate at much lower temperatures.

All electrical equipment works most efficiently at the voltage for which it was designed. A 60-watt lamp designed for a 240-volt circuit will have a working resistance given by eqn. 8. Thus—

$$R = \frac{240 \times 240}{60} = 960 \text{ ohms}$$

Assuming this resistance remains the same when the lamp is transferred to a 120-volt supply (in fact the resistance varies with the temperature), then the power consumed will be—

$$W = \frac{120 \times 120}{960} = 15 \text{ W}$$

So only a quarter of the correct power would be used and the amount of heat developed would not be enough to give more than a dull glow. This is why torches dim when the voltage of the dry battery falls off with long usage.

Electromagnets. A current passing through a wire not only generates heat but also sets up a *magnetic field* around the wire. A magnetic field is a system of lines of force which will act on a magnet. The presence of this field can be seen by passing a fairly heavy current through a wire threaded through a flat sheet of card as in Fig. 18.12. Iron filings sprinkled on the card will arrange themselves in circles round the wire along the paths of the lines of force. Instead of iron filings a small pocket compass may be used. By marking the positions of the north and south poles as it is moved round the wire the field again will be found to be circular. The direction of the field, that is the direction in which it will push the north pole of a magnet, is found by the corkscrew rule. This says that, if you imagine you are driving a corkscrew in the direction of flow of the current the direction of the field is the same as the direction of rotation of the handle.

As the magnetic field around a single wire is often rather weak, the wire is wound into a coil called a *solenoid* to obtain

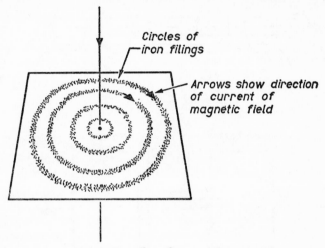

Circles of
iron filings

Arrows show direction
of current of
magnetic field

Fig. 18.12

a force strong enough to operate electric bells, relays, clutches, and electromagnets. As all the turns are wound in the same direction, the fields set up by each turn reinforce each other to make a single field as shown by the dotted lines in Fig. 18.13. The north pole of such a coil can be found by placing the fingers of the right hand round the coil in the direction in which the current is flowing. The extended thumb will then point toward the north pole. Check that this is so by placing a small compass at each end of the coil. Now put a core of soft iron into the coil and see how the compass needle is still further deflected as a result of the rise in magnetic field strength due to the presence of the core. Most electromagnets have such a core to make the best use of the current flowing through them.

A common application of electromagnets in a printing works is the starting button on a machine using high-voltage supply. An electromagnetic relay, as shown in Fig. 18.14, is

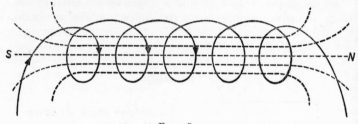

FIG. 18.13

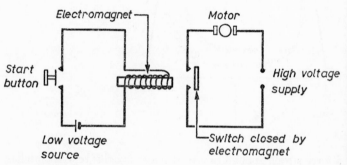

FIG. 18.14

interposed between the starting button and the main supply to the motor so that the operator cannot come into direct contact with the high-voltage circuit. By pressing the starter button he merely switches on a low-voltage supply which then attracts a piece of soft iron which acts as a second switch for the motor circuit itself.

Electricity in Liquids. When the ends of two wires connected to a battery and milliammeter in series are dipped into *distilled* water either no current at all or only a very small one will flow in the circuit. A few drops of sulphuric acid added and stirred in will cause a sharp rise in current to be registered on the ammeter, while bubbles form at one or both wires. A similar rise in current will take place if acids other than sulphuric or if soluble salts are added to distilled water.

Liquids which conduct electricity are called *electrolytes* and their ability to conduct electricity results from the process of ionization described in Chapter 11. In water, sulphuric acid molecules divide into two positive hydrogen ions and one negative sulphate ion as shown in Fig. 18.15. If the metal

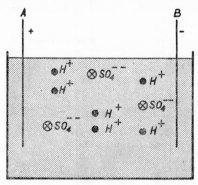

FIG. 18.15

plate A is now made positive (called the *anode*) and the plate B negative (called the *cathode*) by connecting them to a battery, the anode will attract the negative ions and the cathode the positive ions. Arriving at A the negative ions will give up their charge and then either combine with the metal of the plate to form a sulphate or, if the metal will not permit that, they will combine with the hydrogen of the water to re-form sulphuric acid, causing oxygen gas to be given off. The hydrogen ions arriving at B will be neutralized by receiving an electron from the plate and will be given off as hydrogen gas. As each negative ion carries two electrons and the hydrogen ions are each only one short there should be twice as much hydrogen formed as there is oxygen.

That this is true is shown by using the type of voltammeter (quite different from a voltmeter) shown diagrammatically in Fig. 18.16. With the anode and cathode both made of platinum, any current sent through dilute sulphuric acid in the instrument will cause twice as much hydrogen to appear in the right-hand tube as there will be oxygen in the left-hand

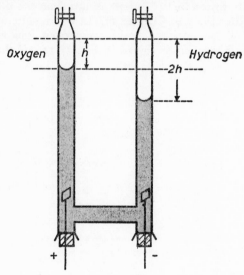

FIG. 18.16

tube. Repeating the experiment with copper instead of platinum electrodes, it will be found that hydrogen is given off in the right-hand tube but no oxygen is formed. Instead a slight blue colour due to the formation of copper sulphate appears near the anode. This is due to the SO_4^{--} ions combining with atoms of copper from the plate.

Depositing Metals. If copper sulphate solution with the addition of a little sulphuric acid is used as the electrolyte, the positive ions formed will be copper ions instead of hydrogen ions. So when the current flows, atoms of copper will be released at the cathode to form a copper facing on the plate and the copper lost from the solution will be continuously replaced by copper dissolved by the negative ions from the anode. This is the principle used in electrotyping and electroplating to build up printing surfaces of various metals, including the preparation of bimetallic and trimetallic plates

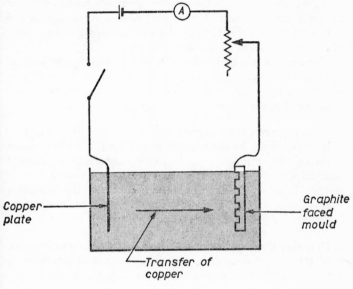

Copper plate

Graphite faced mould

Transfer of copper

FIG. 18.17

used in lithography. The electrolyte must be a salt of the metal to be deposited and the anode must also be of the same metal.

EXPERIMENT 2. TO MAKE A SIMPLE ELECTROTYPE

Apparatus. A small area of type; paraffin wax; graphite; copper plate; beaker of saturated copper sulphate solution; battery; ammeter; variable resistance; switch.

The type is impressed into the softened paraffin wax to form a mould which is then carefully faced all over with graphite to form a conducting surface. This mould is then made the cathode of a plating bath set up as in Fig. 18.17. Care should be taken to secure a good connexion to the graphite facing and to adjust the current to a value at which the copper is deposited in a solid film. The current is then allowed to flow an hour or two to allow a sufficient thickness of copper to build up, after which the mould is removed from the bath and the wax melted to free the copper shell formed.

If great care is used in the above experiment it can be shown by weighing the plates before and after the passage of the current that the weight lost by the anode is equal to the weight of copper deposited on the cathode.

The amount of metal which will be deposited by the passage of an electric current can be calculated with the help of laws discovered by the great British scientist Michael Faraday and known as Faraday's laws. These say—

1. The weight of any substance liberated in electrolysis is proportional to the amount of electricity that has passed through the solution (that is, to the strength of the current multiplied by the time during which it was passing).

2. This weight is also proportional to the chemical equivalent of the substance (that is, to its atomic weight divided by the valency—Chapter 3).

Denoting the weight deposited by M, the current in amps by I, the time in seconds by t, and the equivalent weight by e, we see that M must be proportional to $I \times t \times e$. In fact—

$$M = 0.0000104 \times I \times t \times e \text{ grammes} \qquad . \text{ (10)}$$

The factor 0.0000104 is the weight in grammes of hydrogen liberated by a current of one ampere flowing for one second. Multiplied by the equivalent weight of a substance this factor gives the weight in grammes of that substance which will be liberated by one amp in one second. This weight is called the *electrochemical equivalent* of the substance and if we represent it by the letter z we can write—

$$M = z \times I \times t \qquad . \qquad . \qquad . \text{ (11)}$$

as the equation normally used to find the amount of metal

which will be deposited in a given time. Some typical values
for the electrochemical equivalent are—

Copper (cupric) .	. 0·000329 gm
Nickel . .	. 0·000304 gm
Silver . .	. 0·001118 gm
Tin (stannous) .	. 0·000615 gm

If a current of 30 amps passes through a solution of copper
sulphate for two hours the weight of copper deposited will be—

$$M = 0·000329 \times 30 \times 2 \times 60 \times 60 = 71·15 \text{ gm}$$

In modern practice electrotypes are made by taking a
mould in plastic sheet which is then sprayed with silver nitrate
and a reducing agent to form a conducting face of silver. The
mould is then given a thin plating of nickel to give a hard-
wearing printing surface, followed by a deposited shell of
copper. The back of the copper is then tinned to give good
bonding to the backing metal which is poured molten into the
shell and allowed to solidify to give it mechanical strength.

Electronic Controls. There are very many other applications of electricity in the printing industry, especially in the
field of electronic control, electronic engraving, etc. Most of
these depend on the emission of electrons from metals under
various conditions. Discussion of the principles involved is
beyond the space limitations of this book, but adequate treatment for printers will be found in the books mentioned below.

THINGS TO LEARN

1. An object may become charged by friction, rapid
separation, sudden change of pressure, heat, or chemical
action.

2. Like electric charges repel, unlike charges attract.

3. An electric current is the movement of electrons in a
conductor.

4. *Ohm's Law.* The current in a conductor is proportional
to the voltage across it and inversely proportional to the
resistance of the conductor, provided the temperature remains
constant.

5. *Faraday's Laws*. (*a*) The weight of a substance liberated in electrolysis is proportional to the quantity of electricity passed.

(*b*) This weight is also proportional to the chemical equivalent of the substance.

OTHER BOOKS TO READ

L. S. POWELL, *Electricity and Magnetism* (Pitman)
R. C. WALKER, *Photoelectric Cells in Industry* (Pitman)
Handbook of Electroplating (Canning)
Lithography 1960 (Pergamon)

EXERCISES

1. Static electricity is a constant problem in the printing and paper-making industries. (*a*) State possible causes; (*b*) suggest various possible methods of dealing with the problem. (Lp Mc/1959/Fin.)

2. Your electrical supply has a voltage of 100. Is it safe to plug in a 1 kw electric fire in a 5-amp plug? Give the reason for your answer.
(E and S/1960/Int.)

3. (*a*) Give the definition of the following terms: (i) volt; (ii) ampere; (iii) watt; (iv) horse-power. (*b*) A motor rated at 2 h.p. 460 volts is used to drive a machine. How much would it cost per hour to run with electricity costing 4d. per unit? (E and S/1958/Int.)

4. Explain briefly the theory of a copper-plating cell.
(E and S/1958/Int.)

5. What is meant by the term electrolysis? How is this process used in the production of an electrotype printing plate?
(Lp Mc/1960/Fin.)

6. (*a*) Explain the difference between the conduction of electric current flowing through: (i) a copper wire; and (ii) a solution of copper sulphate. (*b*) State (i) Ohm's law; and (ii) Faraday's laws of electrolysis.
(E and S/1959/Fin.)

7. State Faraday's laws of electrolysis. What conclusion can be drawn from the laws regarding the cost of the current consumed if: (*a*) the required thickness of the deposit is to be doubled; (*b*) silver is to be deposited instead of copper; (*c*) the current density is increased?
(E and S/1958/Fin.)

8. State Ohm's law. If three parallel resistances of 200, 40, and 50 ohms are connected to a 250-volt supply what will be the total power consumed and what current will flow in each resistance?

CHAPTER 19

PAPER PROBLEMS

WITHOUT paper there might never have been a printing industry—certainly it would not have reached its present level of output. Paper is made from natural fibres and so there can be quite wide variations between different makings of the same type of paper. These variations, together with the different requirements for individual jobs, demand that we should not take paper on trust but should be able to check its suitability for the work in hand.

Before looking at the means of testing available, it is necessary to get a few facts about paper itself—but to learn about papermaking you will have to consult a specialist book.

WHAT PAPER IS

Paper is a mat or felt of vegetable fibres, composed mainly of cellulose, to which a number of other substances are added to make it suitable for printing, writing, wrapping, insulating electrical equipment, etc. Many types of fibre are used in paper, but in this country the most common are wood, linen, cotton, esparto, and straw. All the fibres obtained from these sources are very thin tubes with an outside diameter of 0·01 to 0·05 mm and ranging from 1 mm in length to as long as 30 mm in a few cases.

When the fibres are "beaten" in water or are refined, their walls are made capable of holding more water and often are split into very fine shreds—a process known as fibrillation. The water absorbency of the fibres is here modified by *engine sizing*, which has little effect on oil absorbency. Rosin is dissolved in caustic soda and the solution added to the pulp. A further addition of alum is then made to precipitate patches of rosin on the fibres, so giving them a waterproof coating over part of the surface area. An overdose of alum at this stage may give the completed paper a low pH and cause difficulty during printing.

The pulp is also coloured and loaded in the beater. Colour is obtained by adding dyes or pigments similar to those used in printing inks. *Loading* is the addition of finely powdered mineral matter such as china clay or titanium dioxide to increase the opacity of the finished sheet. The white mineral particles fill in the spaces between the fibres, which are quite transparent, and help to scatter light trying to pass through the paper. Loading also increases the smoothness of the paper surface and modifies its absorbency. On the other hand loading reduces the mechanical strength of the paper—hence the poor strength of imitation arts, which may have as much as 30 per cent mineral matter.

Once the pulp and other ingredients have been mixed, the slurry passes to the papermaking machine where it is poured on to a very fine wire mesh through which most of the water drains away. Owing to the high speed at which this mesh moves a large proportion of the fibres tends to settle almost parallel to the direction of travel. Because the fibres thicken rather than lengthen when they absorb moisture, all machine-made papers expand more at right angles to the machine direction with increasing moisture content than they do along it. This is why a sheet of paper wetted on one side curls around the machine direction and why the strength of the sheet is different parallel and at right angles to a given edge.

After the removal of more water by suction and pressure the resulting mat of paper fibre and other materials is dried by passing it over a large number of heated drums. There is a lot of shrinkage in this part of the process, which sets up considerable internal stress. Such stress has to be relieved later by allowing the paper to take up more moisture and mature. If this is not done the paper may curl when on the printing machine.

Part of the way along the drying section the paper may be *surface sized* by the addition of a thin coating of starch, latex, sodium alginate, or a derivative of cellulose. This treatment firmly anchors the looser fibres to the surface of the paper giving a smoother texture and reducing fluffing. In the case of papers for varnishing it reduces the amount of varnish absorbed.

Other surface treatments include super-calendering, coating, and tub-sizing.

Super-calendering gives the paper a smooth surface by passing the damped web through a succession of rollers. The paper is compressed and loose fibres on the surface forced to lie flat. It is the deformation of fibres in this way which sometimes causes fluffing during printing.

Coating is the deposition on the surface of a layer of fine mineral powder to fill up irregularities and produce the very smooth surface needed for fine half-tone screens. The powder is suspended in an alkaline solution of casein which gives the paper a high pH. In some cases coatings may include reducible sulphur (e.g. lithopone) which will cause trouble through the tarnishing of bronze and "gold" inks.

Tub-sizing is the addition to the surface of a thin film of gelatin, sometimes with starch, to reduce the sideways absorption called feathering when the paper is written on. It may give the paper a low surface pH.

When the paper is finally sheeted, the sheeting machine deals with up to five reels at once. This means that the inclusion of a defective reel will lead to the presence of a defective sheet at regular intervals in the ream, so ten consecutive sheets should be taken when sampling paper.

Keeping the Same Size. One of the greatest difficulties of the printer is keeping paper the same size during successive printings. This is due to the fact that the paper changes its moisture content to bring it in balance (equilibrium) with the surrounding atmosphere. If the sheet takes up moisture the fibres will expand, causing the sheet to stretch; if it loses moisture the fibres contract and the sheet gets smaller. The extent of this change in size will depend on the amount of moisture gained or lost, on the type of fibre and the proportion of loading. The change may be up to ten times greater across the machine direction as along it.

A simple way of making a rough comparison between the dimensional stability of one paper and another is shown in Fig. 19.1. Here a ten-inch strip, cut across the machine direction, is held between a fixed clamp and one fixed to a pulley and a pointer so that the pointer moves ten or twenty times as far as the paper stretches. By comparing the amounts the pointer moves when strips of different papers are completely wetted, a comparison is obtained between their dimensional stabilities. Recently it has been shown that this comparison is a valid one for all conditions.

One obvious result of a change in size between one printing and the next is loss of register. What happens can be seen from

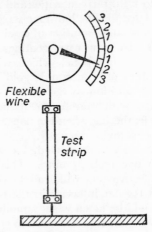

FIG. 19.1. TESTING THE DIMENSIONAL STABILITY OF PAPER

Fig. 19.2. A block of colour printed in the position *AB* will move to the position *CD* if the sheet takes up more moisture through a rise in the relative humidity of the machine room. But the next colour will still be in the position *AB* and will not register.

A less obvious result is the development of curl or wavy edges. When a stack of paper is moved to an atmosphere of higher relative humidity the edges of the sheet will absorb extra moisture and become damper than the centre. The same thing will happen when a stack of cold paper is exposed to the atmosphere of a warm room. In this case the cooling of the air in the neighbourhood of the stack will create an area of high relative humidity around the edges of the paper. When the edges take up extra moisture they become longer than the rest of the sheet and this extra length is taken up by the edges becoming wavy. A stack brought into an atmosphere of lower relative humidity will become drier at the edges than it is in the centre and again wave or curl will occur. These two conditions can be seen by pressing the edges of one

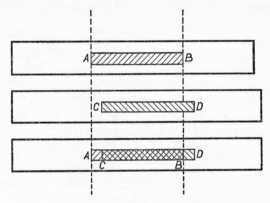

FIG. 19.2. LOSS OF REGISTER

sheet between damp pieces of blotting paper and treating the centre of another sheet in the same way.

Checking the Balance. From what has been said so far it will be clear that the main thing a printer needs to know is whether or not the paper he wants to use is in balance with the relative humidity of the place in which he is going to use it. To make it easier for this to be checked directly, PATRA has designed an instrument called the PATRA PET (Paper Equilibrium Tester). It is a sword-shaped piece of metal which can be inserted through the wrapping of a ream of paper. Pressure on the lever A (Fig. 19.3) raises two small blades, C and D, with inking pads around them, to make two reference marks exactly 20 in. apart in the sheet above. The sheet is then removed from the ream and hung in the room for fifteen minutes to reach a moisture balance with the surrounding atmosphere. The inspection windows *E* and *F* are then placed over the reference marks so that the scale in the window *F* shows how much the distance between the marks has changed. A little experience in the use of the PET will soon indicate the maximum permissible change for each class of work.

Testing Paper. Methods of testing paper for its suitability for various printing processes and uses are the subject of a

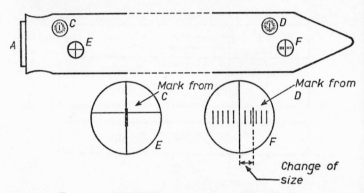

FIG. 19.3. THE PATRA PAPER EQUILIBRIUM TESTER

voluminous literature to which the most useful guidance can be obtained from the reports of PATRA conferences, the PATRA paper-buying guides, and the publications of the Technical section of the British Paper and Board Makers' Association. As paper properties vary with a large number of factors, care is needed in selecting a fair sample for each test and in ensuring that testing is carried out in standard conditions. The main precautions to be observed are—

(i) Samples should be taken from a number of reels or reams, ten consecutive sheets being taken from each ream;

(ii) care should be taken that samples are not contaminated by undue handling or contact with other materials;

(iii) testing should where possible be carried out in a room kept at constant temperature and humidity.

While the tests given below are by no means all those possible, they do include those most likely to be of use to a commercial printer and which require a minimum of apparatus. They cover the paper tests incorporated in the standard PATRA test bench procedure.

Furnish. The presence of mechanically prepared wood fibre is very quickly revealed by brushing on the sample a drop of the stain phloroglucinol. This reacts with the lignin which is retained by mechanical wood and gives a colour ranging from pink to deep red according to the amount of mechanical wood fibre present. More detailed information about the types of fibre can be obtained by macerating the paper in a large quantity of distilled water to separate the fibres and examining them under a medium-powered microscope. Identification is made easier by the addition of the iodine and zinc chloride reagent known as Herzberg stain. This colours esparto deep violet, chemical wood pale blue, straw blue, rag red, and mechanical wood yellow. The general appearance of the main fibres under the microscope is shown in Plate IV.

Substance. The rather confusing method of giving the substance of paper in pounds per ream of a particular size is now being replaced by stating the number of grammes per square metre (g.s.m.). This allows comparison to be made between sheets of different sizes without recourse to conversion tables. To find the substance in g.s.m. a templet is used to cut a sample exactly 10 cm square, i.e. exactly one-hundredth of a square metre in area. The sample can then be weighed on a quadrant balance which gives the g.s.m. directly or on a chemical balance, in which case the weight obtained is multiplied by one hundred to find the g.s.m. For instance a sample weighing 0·854 gm would have come from a sheet weighing 85·4 g.s.m.

Caliper. Changes in the caliper or thickness of sheets during the running of a job can lead to difficulties with impression, register, feeding, and delivery. Variation in thickness can be checked by measuring individual sheets with a micrometer loaded to give a pressure of $7\frac{1}{2}$ lb per sq. in. This standard pressure is necessary to prevent errors due to the compressibility of paper. An average value of the caliper is obtained by taking the mean of ten micrometer readings taken on piles of paper each eight sheets thick. Dial micrometers made specially for the purpose are preferable to the screw type for this work.

Smoothness. One property of paper obviously of great importance is its surface smoothness. On it will depend the fineness of the half-tone screen that can be used, the amount of ink required and the printing pressure.

One instrument used to measure smoothness is the Bendtsen smoothness tester which measures the rate at which air escapes from underneath a metal ring placed on the surface of the paper. The smoother the paper the fewer will be the gaps between the ring and its surface and the slower will be the flow of air between the two. To obtain readings which are really comparable a constant pressure must be maintained in the air supply and also between the ring and the paper. This Bendtsen tester can be used to measure softness by comparing the rate of flow for two different pressures between ring and paper. The difference will increase with increasing softness of the paper.

A different principle is employed in the Chapman tester. Here the paper is placed in contact with a glass prism illuminated from above. Two photoelectric cells compare the amount of light reflected by the paper as a whole with that reflected from those parts of the surface which are actually touching the glass. The closer together these two values are the smoother the surface of the paper will be. Again softness can be measured by taking readings at two different pressures. One great advantage of the Chapman instrument is that the contact between the paper and the glass can be inspected by eye and the distribution of the irregularities can be seen.

Both these instruments need highly-skilled operation and are not very suitable for routine control. Smoothness can be estimated by visual inspection under a stereomicroscope with $\times 20$ magnification, as supplied with the PATRA test bench. This allows the surface to be seen in relief, an effect made all the clearer by illuminating the paper at a very low angle (as in Fig. 19.4). A special blue ink may also be applied to show microcontours of the surface.

Oil Absorbency. The final appearance of a print will depend to a very considerable degree on the rate at which the vehicle of the ink is absorbed into the paper. This, in turn, depends on the number and size of the "pores" or capillary openings in the surface as well as on the viscosity of the vehicle and the concentration of pigment. The smoothness of a paper is not necessarily an indication of its absorbency, as a machine-finished paper may be far less absorbent than a coated paper. We must have some method of measuring oil absorbency if

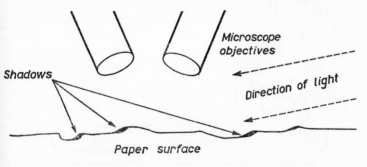

FIG. 19.4. EXAMINATION OF SMOOTHNESS

we are to avoid powdering, loss of gloss, or strike-through owing to the paper being too absorbent, and set-off owing to it not being absorbent enough. To meet this need PATRA has developed a surface-oil absorption tester which gives a reasonable comparison between papers of the same type after a little practice.

The general layout of the instrument is shown in Fig. 19.5. A drop of paraffin oil of constant size and viscosity is allowed to fall on a brass cylinder held by a catch at the top of an inclined ramp which is covered with a rubber offset blanket. The cylinder is released to run down the ramp so that the oil is first spread into a thin film between cylinder and blanket. It then passes over the test paper leaving a patch of oil on its surface. A stopwatch is started as soon as the oil touches the paper and is stopped when 75 per cent of it has been absorbed.

The average of ten readings is taken as the oil-absorption time of the paper.

As a general guide to printers, PATRA gives a minimum oil-absorption time of 30 seconds for gloss printing, varnishing, or bronzing on any type of paper. For coated papers 10 seconds is given as the lower limit for avoiding powdering and 200 seconds as the upper limit if set-off is to be avoided.

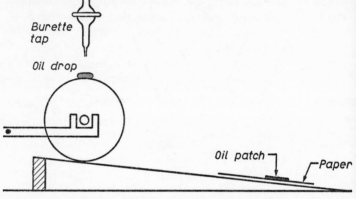

FIG. 19.5. SURFACE OIL ABSORPTION TESTER

There are other ways of measuring the oil absorbency of paper but the PATRA method is the one accepted by the printing industry for routine control purposes.

Opacity. It is necessary for any printed matter to be free of interference from type or illustrations printed on the reverse side of the sheet. The amount of light which gets through the sheet depends on its opacity or ability to block the passage of light. Opacity may be stated numerically as the percentage of the light falling on the sheet which is scattered back by the fibres and particles of loading. It can be measured in a printing works fairly simply by the EEL opacimeter, of which the principle is shown in Fig. 19.6. Sheets of the paper to be tested are placed on the aperture D in a pile thick enough to be completely opaque. The galvanometer to which the photo-electric cell F is connected is set to give a full-scale deflexion of

100 divisions. If the pile is now reduced to a single sheet backed by the light-absorbing cap E, the deflexion of the galvano-meter will fall to a lower value because less light is scattered back into the light-collecting box. If the new deflexion is 94 then the opacity of the paper is 94 per cent. Comparison of a

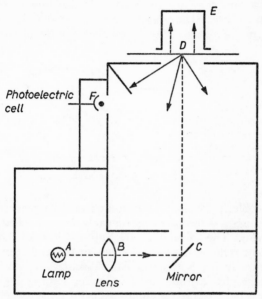

FIG. 19.6. THE EEL OPACIMETER

single sheet with a pile of the same paper eliminates the effect on the photoelectric cell of varying colour between different papers.

For more routine checks on the opacity of paper PATRA has devised an *opacity indicator* made up of a series of half-sheets of standard opacities ranging in steps down from 100 per cent. These are interleaved with heavily printed sheets on which the test paper can be laid alongside the standard half-sheets until one of corresponding opacity is found. The comparison is made by judging which of the standard papers gives the same amount of show-through as the sheet under test.

Opacity should not be less than 95 per cent for any job and not below 98 per cent for good-quality work.

Gloss. The gloss of a paper surface or of a film of ink depends on the amount of specular reflection from it. A numerical value for gloss can be obtained by measuring this specular reflection and comparing it with that from some standard polished surface. The glossmeter used for this is shown in outline in Fig. 19.7. The instrument is first placed on a

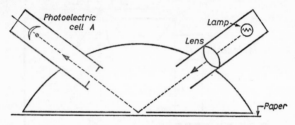

FIG. 19.7. A GLOSSMETER

polished black tile and the current from the photo-electric cell *A* causes a deflexion of the galvanometer attached to the instrument. The galvanometer is adjusted to read 100. The tile is now replaced by the paper under test and the reading obtained, say 83, is the specular reflection (or gloss) as a percentage of that from the tile. As the limbs of the instrument are both set at the same angle to the specimen, only light reflected specularly is measured.

Surface Strength. Weaknesses in the surface structure of paper will show themselves during printing operations in one of three ways. In the case of uncoated papers the tack of the ink may pull individual fibres away from the surface and transfer them to the printing surface or offset blanket where they will cause blemishes on succeeding prints—this is called *fluffing*. With coated papers poor adhesion of the coating to the body may lead to pieces of the coating coming away—this is called *pick*. If the break takes place in the fibres below the coating the trouble is known as *splitting*. The process leading to these difficulties is a complicated one depending on the paper, machine speed, ink tack, and other factors. The best method of testing surface strength at present available is the IGT Printability Tester developed by the Dutch counterpart of PATRA (Fig. 19.8). The paper to be tested is attached as a narrow strip to the segment on the right which is pulled down at increasing speed against the inked cylinder on the left. Examination of the strip shows immediately whether the paper has picked and indicates the speed at which picking began.

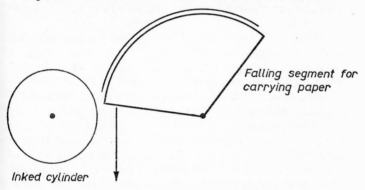

Falling segment for carrying paper

Inked cylinder

FIG. 19.8. THE IGT PRINTABILITY TESTER

As the cylinder can be covered either with an ink of known tack or with the ink proposed for a given job, and both speed and printing pressure varied, the instrument is very flexible in its applications. It is, however, rather expensive.

An alternative, but less satisfactory, method of measuring surface strength, is offered by the Dennison wax test. Sticks of blended wax with graded strengths of adhesion are provided in a numbered series. To make a test the ends of suitable waxes are melted, pressed down on the paper and left to set for at least five minutes. When they are lifted from the paper they are examined to see if any of the paper surface has been pulled away by the wax. The number of the weakest wax to rupture the surface is given as the pick number. The main weakness of the wax test is that it is made in static conditions and at a temperature which may affect the constituents of the paper. It is, however, able to range papers in order of surface strength for many uses.

pH. The pH of a paper surface can be found by smearing a drop of indicator over it with a clean piece of glass and comparing the colour obtained with the colours of a series of slides specially prepared for the purpose. These colour slides are given a series of numbers, instead of pH values, called the PATRA pH index. It is better, however, to make an extract from the paper (as set out in Chapter 11) to get a reliable guide to its pH.

Differences between the pH of stock and coating make this method unsuitable for coated papers. For these 0·1 gm of the coating is scraped off and stirred into 15 ml of distilled water. The pH may then be measured as above after ten minutes. The cloudiness of such extracts makes the use of a pH meter more suitable than any indicator method.

In letterpress printing, paper with a low pH will not slow down seriously the drying of ink unless the relative humidity is in the region of 75 per cent (Fig. 11.4). Papers with a pH of 5 or more are safe. In lithography, however, the constant presence of damping water makes low pH a threat to drying at any relative humidity. It should be noted also that very alkaline surfaces can increase the pH of the damping water above the safety level. To be on the safe side lowest figures for lithographic papers should be pH 5 for uncoated, pH 6 for machine coated, and pH 7·5 for other coated papers.

Reducible Sulphur. Tarnishing of so-called gold inks and bronze often arises from the presence in the paper or board of reducible sulphur, which can react with the copper in the powdered brass or bronze to form black copper sulphide. As little as two parts per million may be sufficient to cause tarnishing in acid conditions. The presence of sulphur in this form can be detected by heating one gramme of the paper in a flask with 10 ml of phosphoric acid, 20 ml distilled water and a few pieces of zinc. The mouth of the flask is covered with filter paper soaked in lead acetate solution and the temperature kept at 110°C for one hour. The presence of reducible sulphur is shown by blackening of the filter paper, due to the formation of lead sulphide. The amount of blackening which takes place can be used to estimate the quantity of sulphur in the paper or board under test.

Strength Tests. There is a whole range of equipment available for measuring tensile strength, tear resistance, folding endurance and so on, Most of it is rather expensive and only the larger printing works are able to make adequate use of it at present. Details of this equipment and its operation can be found in the books recommended below.

OTHER BOOKS TO READ

Paper Making (British Paper and Board Makers' Association)
PATRA Paper Buying Guides
Reports of PATRA Letterpress and Lithographic Conferences

EXERCISES

1. Describe with the aid of diagrams: (*a*) esparto fibres and (*b*) mechanical wood fibres which are used in the manufacture of paper.
(Lp Mc/1960/Fin.)

2. Describe briefly the following processes in the manufacture of paper by machine: (*a*) coating; (*b*) loading; (*c*) sizing. State clearly the purpose of each of these processes. (Wh/1961/Fin.)

3. List, and give the properties of, three fibres, one loading material, and one sizing material used in paper making. (Litho/1960/Int.)

4. Explain why a coated paper may have a much faster surface oil absorption than a machine-finished paper. Give the principle of operation of an instrument which will enable comparison to be made between the surface-oil absorption of different samples of paper.

5. List the materials used to give increased opacity to paper in the manufacturing process. How would you specify the opacity required when placing an order for paper?

6. State what you understand by the following terms in connexion with paper testing: (*a*) substance; (*b*) machine direction; (*c*) opacity. Suggest simple methods which you could use to obtain, with some degree of accuracy, the above properties. (Lp Mc/1961/Fin.)

7. What do you understand by the terms picking, splitting, and fluffing applied to paper? Outline a test which will compare the surface strength of a number of different samples of paper of the same type.

8. (*a*) Describe fully the effect of loose paper fibres on the completed impression.

(*b*) How can loose fibres on the surface be assessed by instruments?
(Litho/1961/Fin.)

CHAPTER 20

CARRIERS FOR COLOUR

IN all the major printing processes, and most of the minor ones, a coloured image is transferred to the stock in the form of a liquid, often very viscous, which we call ink. Once the image has been impressed on the stock, be it paper, plastic, metal, or other material, we have to make the image permanent by drying the ink. As we shall see later, the word drying is not used in the ordinary sense which applies to drying clothes (except in one or two cases). What is meant here by drying is the formation of a film of colour which will remain bonded to the stock in such a way that its shape will remain unchanged for as long as it is needed.

Most printing inks, therefore, have two main components, tiny solid particles of coloured material which are called the *pigment*, which will be discussed in the next chapter, and a liquid called the *vehicle* (or carrier). This name has been given to the liquid because it is needed to convey the pigment from the duct to the stock. Then the liquid must be turned into a solid as quickly as possible. In other words the pigment rides in a vehicle to its final destination.

In addition to these main ingredients inks may include driers to speed up solidification of the film, substances to give better bonding to the base material, and other additives to meet special requirements.

Methods of Drying. Choice of the liquid to act as the vehicle will depend on a number of factors of which the speed at which the film is required to dry is one of the most important. Methods of turning the liquid ink into a solid include one or more of the following—

Absorption: removing the liquid from the film by allowing it to soak into the paper.

Evaporation: allowing the liquid to turn into a vapour, either by using a very low boiling point substance or by heating the ink film after it has been applied.

Oxidation and Polymerization: a combined action in which

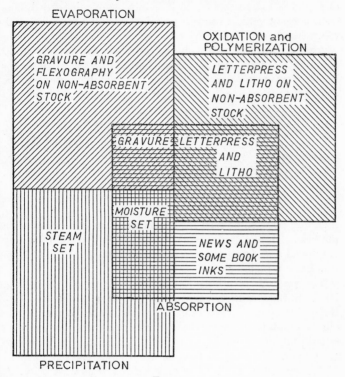

FIG. 20.1

molecules of the vehicle undergo chemical changes which turn them into a solid.

Precipitation: in which a second liquid, usually water, comes in contact with the vehicle causing the colouring matter and resin to be precipitated on the paper.

The way these possible methods of drying an ink film are used in combination are shown in a simplified form in Fig. 20.1.

There are a few other methods in use for specialized applications but the four noted above cover the vast majority of printed products. For each drying method a different type of liquid is most suitable, so it is most convenient to discuss each class of vehicle used in printing inks in connexion with the method by which it dries.

Absorption. As was seen in Chapter 8, whenever a liquid comes in contact with a porous material, such as paper or board, surface tension will cause some of the liquid to be drawn into the spaces between fibres and loading. Absorption

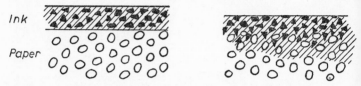

FIG. 20.2. THE PROGRESS OF ABSORPTION DRYING

therefore plays some part in the drying of an ink on any such material. In newspaper work it is the only method of drying employed and, in some letterpress and litho printing, absorption plays a major part.

The progress of absorption drying can be seen from Fig. 20.2. Surface tension carries the vehicle into the capillary tubes of the paper structure until the particles of pigment come close enough together for the spaces between them to exert an equal pull on the liquid, at which point no more will go into the paper. For this to happen very quickly, as it must in high-speed work, the vehicle must be of very low viscosity. A suitable type of liquid is to be found among the paraffins, also called mineral oils. These are chains of carbon atoms combined with the maximum possible number of hydrogen atoms (Fig. 20.3) and form a series of compounds ranging from methane, or marsh gas CH_4, which contains only one carbon atom, to solid paraffin waxes with scores of carbon atoms in the chain. The paraffins occur in the crude oil found in the earth, those with the most suitable chain length and viscosity being sorted out by fractional distillation at the oil refinery.

The viscosity we require is about the same as that of oil used to lubricate a car engine.

The film of ink left on the surface of a newspaper is never really dry, consisting of a mixture of pigment and oil with a little resin included to improve adhesion to the paper. It looks dull and lifeless with very little light reflected specularly from its surface. But the very high speed at which absorption takes place makes it a method we would like to use for all types of work. Quick-setting inks are made, therefore, with a

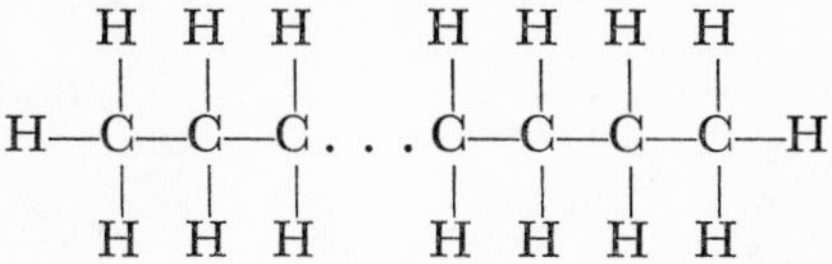

$$
\begin{array}{ccccccc}
& \text{H} & \text{H} & \text{H} & \text{H} & \text{H} & \text{H} & \text{H} \\
& | & | & | & & | & | & | & | \\
\text{H}-&\text{C}-&\text{C}-&\text{C}\ldots&\text{C}-&\text{C}-&\text{C}-&\text{C}-\text{H} \\
& | & | & | & & | & | & | & | \\
& \text{H} & \text{H} & \text{H} & \text{H} & \text{H} & \text{H} & \text{H}
\end{array}
$$

FIG. 20.3. MOLECULAR STRUCTURE OF MINERAL OILS

mixed vehicle, part of which is absorbed or evaporated immediately and the remainder of which is a very viscous varnish which remains on the surface with the pigment to dry more slowly by oxidation and polymerization to a hard, glossy film.

Satisfactory results with absorption drying require a proper relationship between the viscosity of the vehicle and the rate of oil absorption by the paper. If the paper does not absorb enough of the vehicle there will be considerable set-off and the ink may fail to dry at all, since mineral oils do not react with the oxygen of the atmosphere (as do the vegetable oils which we shall consider later). On the other hand difficulties can arise if the vehicle is absorbed too completely. This will mean that the pigment is left on the surface without an effective binding agent and thus "powders," coming off when rubbed or setting-off on the underside of the following sheet. This trouble is very common on close-surfaced papers. With more open-surfaced papers like machine-finished, powdering is less common, probably because a substantial part of the pigment is carried down into the structure of the paper with the vehicle. If the paper is too absorbent the result may be strike-through or show-through. The former is the appearance on the other side of the sheet of a stain, in the shape of the printed image, due to the oil going right through the paper. Show-through arises because the oil, which makes the paper more transparent, has penetrated so deeply into the paper that the printed image can be seen clearly from the other side (Fig. 20.4). Each of these troubles reinforces the other and they are sometimes difficult to distinguish on a sheet printed on both sides.

Because the viscosity of the vehicle is increased by a fall in temperature, the vehicle may fail to penetrate sufficiently if the

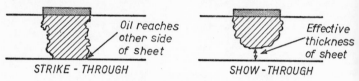

STRIKE - THROUGH   SHOW - THROUGH

Fig. 20.4. Strike-through and Show-through

paper being printed is too cold. Similarly, if the temperature is too high there may be too much penetration.

Use of the PATRA oil-absorption test described in the last chapter will give a good guide to the suitability of a paper for use with an ink which dries partly by absorption.

Oxidation and Polymerization. Most of the inks used in letterpress and lithography are required to dry with a glossy finish which considerably improves the appearance of the finished sheet. To obtain this effect it is necessary to have the pigment held on the surface of the paper in a thin, transparent solid film, which as well as giving a large amount of specular reflection will act as a protective shield for the pigment. Such a solid can be obtained in a few hours by using as the vehicle one of a group of substances usually of vegetable origin known as drying oils.

Drying oils include linseed oil from the flax seed, tung, or china-wood oil from the seeds of a fruit tree, cotton-seed oil, soya-bean oil, perilla oil, and a number of others. All these oils contain compounds of unsaturated fatty acids, which have a carbon chain similar to that of the paraffins but with some of the hydrogen atoms missing—hence the prefix unsaturated. Where the hydrogen atoms are missing there are two links between neighbouring carbon atoms instead of one. It is this double bond, of which there may be more than one in each molecule, which takes part in the chemical reactions responsible for the formation of the solid film. The faster-drying oils, such as tung oil, which also gives a very high gloss, have two such double bonds close together as shown in Fig. 20.5.

In their natural form the oils are not viscous enough for use in a printing ink so they are made into a varnish by

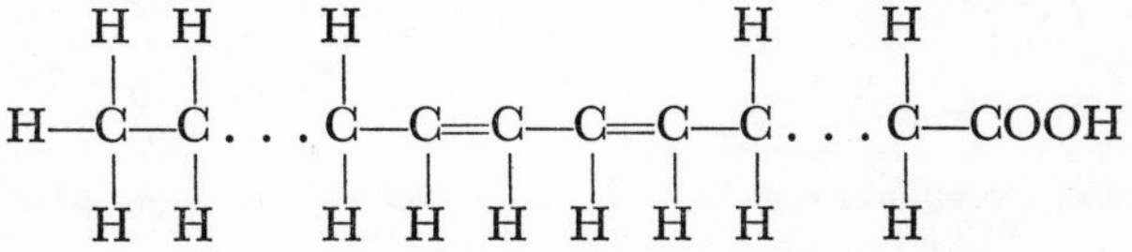

$$
\begin{array}{c}
\text{H}\quad\text{H}\qquad\text{H}\qquad\qquad\qquad\text{H}\qquad\text{H}\\
|\quad\ |\qquad\ |\qquad\qquad\qquad\ |\qquad\ |\\
\text{H—C—C}\ .\ .\ .\ \text{C—C}{=}\text{C—C}{=}\text{C—C}\ .\ .\ .\ \text{C—COOH}\\
|\quad\ |\qquad\ |\quad\ |\quad\ |\quad\ |\quad\ |\quad\ |\qquad\qquad\ |\\
\text{H}\quad\text{H}\qquad\text{H}\quad\text{H}\quad\text{H}\quad\text{H}\quad\text{H}\quad\text{H}\qquad\qquad\text{H}
\end{array}
$$

FIG. 20.5. MOLECULAR STRUCTURE OF THE FASTER DRYING OILS

heating, sometimes under pressure, for varying periods. During this process the molecules begin to polymerize, that is, link up into longer chains, and so become more resistant to flow. The degree of polymerization depends on the length of time for which the heating is continued, and thus the more viscous varnishes, such as those used in lithography, are the result of more prolonged heating than a tint or medium varnish.

When the varnishes prepared in this way are exposed to the atmosphere they react with the oxygen present (the oxygen breaking one link of the double bond) and start a further process of polymerization which makes the varnish solidify into a hard, transparent and flexible material (Fig. 20.6). Left to themselves varnishes take many hours to dry, especially if they are coated on a non-absorbent material such as glass, but the drying time can be reduced very considerably by the addition of driers.

Driers are the salts formed by the metals lead, manganese, cobalt, and cerium with the unsaturated fatty acids, e.g. lead linoleate, cobalt napenthate. Lead and manganese borate are used in paste driers. All these metals have more than one oxide and the lower oxides are more stable than the higher ones. Only very small quantities of drier are needed because they act as *catalysts*, substances which assist a chemical change without undergoing any permanent change themselves. In the first stage of drying the driers act as oxygen carriers transferring atmospheric oxygen to the molecules of drying oil faster than the drying oil can win them for itself. In the later stages the drier seems to help in the formation of the long chains of

Before polymerization　　　　　During polymerization

Fig. 20.6

molecules which lead to the final solidification of the film. It should be noted that the salts used as driers are soapy compounds which do not dry themselves and so an excess of drier may prevent the ink from drying instead of helping it to dry.

Most driers in common use are a combination of salts of lead, manganese, and cobalt. Each of these metals has a slightly different action. Lead is rather slow but helps the drying to take place right through the film of ink. Manganese starts the drying action much more quickly than the other two. Cobalt is the fastest of the three but tends to dry the upper layers of the film more than those nearer the paper. By varying the amount of each the speed of the drying action can be adjusted as required. The fastest time possible with this type of catalyst is about 45 minutes for a linseed oil varnish, but the difficulty caused by ink drying on the rollers prevents us taking advantage of such super-fast drying. A few hours are allowed normally for the final stages of drying, especially since the combination of absorption with the oxidation method gives an ink film stable enough for handling in a few minutes.

In recent years the drying oils which formed the main

vehicle systems for letterpress and lithographic inks have been replaced or supplemented by various types of synthetic resin which give a much more uniform product. The drying action of these resins is similar to that of the natural drying oils and in many inks the resins will be found combined with a certain amount of natural drying oil.

As the first stage of the drying of this type of ink is due to oxidation it is obvious that drying will be retarded if the supply of oxygen is inadequate. When sheets are held very close together—by attraction caused by static electricity, for instance—the flow of air between the sheets in the delivery pile will be cut down very considerably, with the result that oxygen starvation occurs and drying is delayed.

Drying time of an ink on paper and board is also affected by relative humidity, especially when the paper has a low pH value. When the pH value of paper is above five there is a quite small increase in the time the ink takes to dry as the relative humidity rises, but the effect of pH below five is a catastrophic increase in drying time—for lithography at normal relative humidity and for letterpress at relative humidities of 75 per cent and above. From examination of acid papers which have failed to dry it has been found that the metals of the driers in the ink have been transferred into the body of the paper by a chemical reaction between the acid materials on the surface of the paper and the metallic salts in the ink, so leaving the ink on the surface without the requisite amount of drier. This is why it is recommended that the pH of paper should be above five for satisfactory printing results.

In workshop conditions printers are much more concerned with the time an ink will take to dry on a certain paper or board than they are with the drying time of the ink itself apart from the influence of the paper. To find the relative drying time of various ink–paper combinations PATRA have developed a Print Drying Time Tester. This consists essentially of a slowly revolving drum to which can be attached strips of printed paper which are covered with clean sheets of bond. As the drum rotates a heavy stylus moves laterally across it causing wet ink to be transferred to the sheet of bond. The bond thus shows a series of lines set off from each of the printed strips. The more quickly the ink dries the fewer lines will appear on the bond.

Precipitation. The main class of inks using precipitation as the basis of the drying process are the now commonly used moisture-set inks of the letterpress printer. These inks have the great advantage that they are free from the unpleasant odour which arises from the formation of certain peroxides in the oxidation stage of drying of a vegetable oil. The vehicle for this type of ink is one of the substances called diglycols, which are carbon chains with an hydroxyl (OH) group at each end as shown in Fig. 20.7. These solvents will readily dissolve

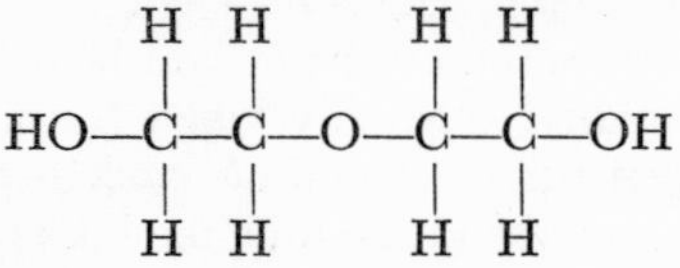

$$\text{HO--}\overset{\displaystyle \overset{H}{|}}{\underset{\displaystyle \underset{H}{|}}{C}}\text{--}\overset{\displaystyle \overset{H}{|}}{\underset{\displaystyle \underset{H}{|}}{C}}\text{--O--}\overset{\displaystyle \overset{H}{|}}{\underset{\displaystyle \underset{H}{|}}{C}}\text{--}\overset{\displaystyle \overset{H}{|}}{\underset{\displaystyle \underset{H}{|}}{C}}\text{--OH}$$

FIG. 20.7. MOLECULAR STRUCTURE OF A DIGLYCOL

certain types of resin under normal conditions. The presence of the two hydroxyl groups, however, makes them take up water very quickly and once they do this they will no longer keep the resin in solution but release it as a solid precipitate. For most moisture-set inks the amount of moisture present in the paper is sufficient to cause precipitation—the difficulty is to prevent the moisture present in the atmosphere from causing precipitation in the duct or on the rollers—but if the amount of moisture in the paper is insufficient a steam jet on the delivery will remedy the difficulty. Moisture-set inks cannot be used with rollers containing gelatin, glue, or other moisture retaining materials, nor can they be used in lithography owing to the constant presence of the fountain solution.

Evaporation. Inks drying by evaporation are used mainly in gravure and in some types of flexography. Although there is a small amount of absorption when these inks are applied to paper or board, it is not an essential part of the drying operation and evaporation inks are suitable for use on completely non-absorbent stock such as plastic films of various kinds.

There is a very wide range of solvents open for use as vehicles for evaporation inks, the choice of a particular solvent being determined by a large number of factors including the type of resin used as a binder for the final dried film. Speed of drying of an evaporation ink depends on the vapour pressure of the solvent used. As a general guide, the lower the boiling point the faster will the solvent evaporate and the less additional heat will be required to accelerate drying. Most of the solvents available, however, are highly inflammable, and so safety considerations often prevent the use of the fastest drying solvent because the *flash point* of the solvent is too low. The flash point is the lowest temperature at which the solvent will form a vapour which will be ignited by a naked flame near the surface of the solvent. In rotogravure, for instance, use of the very great speed of evaporation of benzene is inadvisable because the flash point of benzene is well below normal room temperature. The nature of the printing plate will also limit choice of solvent. It would not be possible, for instance, to use a solvent which dissolved rubber when printing from a rubber plate. Equally the stock will affect the choice of solvent, which in some cases is required to dissolve the upper layer of a plastic film in order to achieve adequate bonding of ink film to stock.

With these and other considerations in mind final choice of a solvent can be made from one or more of the following groups of organic substances—

Hydrocarbons. The most commonly used of these are toluol and xylol, impure forms of the substances toluene and xylene the structure of which is given in Fig. 20.8. These are very good solvents of synthetic resins and will also hold nitrocellulose in solution if it has first been dissolved in one of the other solvents. The boiling range of toluol is 105–111°C and its flash point 5°C. Corresponding figures for xylol are 136–140°C and 24–26°C. These two solvents are in predominant use in gravure magazine work, evaporation being speeded up by passing the printed web over steam-heated drums. The vaporized solvents are drawn off by extraction ducts and the solvent laden air is passed through large containers of charcoal which adsorbs the solvent on its surface. The solvent is then recovered for re-use by heating the charcoal with steam and separating the solvent from the steam by means of a separating column.

Alcohols. The alcohols consist of carbon chain compounds similar to those shown in Fig. 20.3 but with one of the hydrogen atoms replaced by a hydroxyl group. The alcohols range from methyl (wood) alcohol upward. Those of the series in

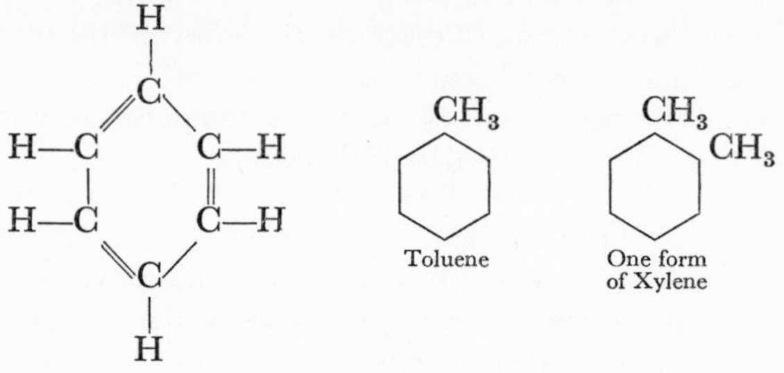

Benzene   Toluene   One form of Xylene

FIG. 20.8. MOLECULAR STRUCTURE OF HYDROCARBONS

most common use are ethyl, propyl, butyl, and amyl (in descending order of volatility) and all are found in evaporation inks and spirit varnishes.

Ketones. The characteristic of the ketones is that one of the atoms in the carbon chain has lost two of its hydrogen atoms and replaced them with an atom of oxygen. Acetone is the most common of the ketones and is in regular use as a solvent. It boils at 56°C and is very inflammable.

Esters. Just as inorganic bases will react with acids to form salts, so alcohols will react with organic acids to form esters. The most common esters found in printing inks are the acetates. They are good solvents both for synthetic resins and for cellulose derivatives.

Most of the evaporation inks consist of the solvent and a synthetic resin or cellulose derivative which acts as a binding agent for holding the pigment on the paper. In some cases evaporation is speeded up by passing the print under infra-red or other heating mechanism and in extreme cases the solvent is actually set on fire by gas jets to secure the highest speeds of drying.

OTHER BOOKS TO READ

H. J. WOLFE, *Printing and Litho Inks* (MacNair-Dorland Co.)
E. A. APPS, *Printing Ink Technology* (L. Hill)
R. F. BOWLES, (Ed.), *Printing Ink Manual* (Heffer)

EXERCISES

1. Describe with the aid of diagrams the stages by which a quickset letterpress or litho ink dries on absorbent stock. What would you expect to be the trouble if the ink film: (*a*) powdered; (*b*) set-off badly?

2. Name the four main methods used for drying a printing ink. Name a suitable type of vehicle for each method.

3. What is meant by the terms boiling range and flash point applied to a solvent for gravure ink? Explain the importance of these properties in the choice of a solvent.

4. Describe the way in which a moisture-set ink dries and the steps taken to make it dry on non-absorbent stock. Why are moisture-set inks unsuitable for use in lithography?

5. Outline the action of driers in a printing ink based on a vegetable oil varnish. What are the main differences between the actions of lead and cobalt driers?

CHAPTER 21

PIGMENTS FOR PRINTING INKS

In printing and in life generally, we tend to take for granted the wide range of colours available to us today. It is easy to forget that the majority of these colours did not exist a hundred years ago. It is a comparatively short time since the printer was only concerned with black ink.

Printing inks normally contain pigments, which are insoluble in water, rather than soluble dyes. Dyes are only used for a number of special purposes, e.g. in news ink to correct the brownish tone of carbon black pigment. There are many coloured substances which do not dissolve in water but only a small proportion of them have the properties to make them useful in printing inks. The more important of these properties are good colour strength, reasonable stability to light and chemicals, fine particle size, and the ability to be dispersed in normal ink vehicles. For a particular ink, a number of special properties may be demanded of a pigment. We will be considering these later in this chapter.

TYPES OF PIGMENTS

Carbon Black. The most important pigment used in printing-ink manufacture and the one that has been known the longest is carbon black. All black inks are pigmented with carbon, the element which is the basic constituent of animal and vegetable materials. If these carbon-containing substances are burnt in air a soot is deposited. If in this process the quantity of air is carefully controlled, large quantities of soot form, of a type which is a most effective black pigment. There are several grades of carbon black obtained by varying the manufacturing conditions. Today vast quantities are produced, largely in the U.S.A., by the ignition of "natural gas," the most volatile fraction of crude oil. The greater proportion of this mixture of gases is methane CH_4. This burns in a limited supply of oxygen according to the equation—

$$CH_4 + O_2 = C + 2H_2O$$

EXPERIMENT 1. TO PREPARE A FORM OF CARBON BLACK

Fill a large round bottom flask with cold water and hold it immediately above the yellow flame of a Bunsen burner (adjusted to exclude air). Scrape off the black deposit and examine. Add a very small quantity of a mineral oil and work in the carbon black with a palette knife. This will now be a crude form of news ink.

Carbon black is a remarkable material. There is no other black pigment with comparable colour strength and, in addition, it is cheap and resistant to light, heat, moisture, and most chemicals.

White Pigments. Originally, naturally occurring substances like china clay and chalk were used but these were generally coarse and gritty. They are now prepared chemically along with other white inorganic pigments which do not occur naturally. Alumina, zinc oxide, lithopone, and titanium dioxide are all widely used in printing inks as pigments and as extenders. Of these, titanium dioxide, a comparative newcomer, has quite outstanding covering power and colour retention. On the other hand, alumina is extremely transparent and has excellent working properties.

EXPERIMENT 2. TO COMPARE THE COVERING POWER OF ALUMINA
AND TITANIUM DIOXIDE

Take approximately equal quantities of the white pigments and work into equal quantities of mid-varnish on a glass plate or slab. When these have been thoroughly mixed to a smooth paste, place a small blob of each varnish about $1\frac{1}{2}$ in. apart on the edge of a piece of white paper. Using a drawdown knife draw the two varnishes across the paper to give films of similar thickness. Repeat the process on a second piece of paper so that the films of varnish both cross a band of solid colour (Fig. 21.1). Compare the effects of the two prints.

Like all mineral pigments, these whites are inclined to be abrasive and an ink containing a large proportion of white will, for instance, greatly reduce the life of an image on a litho plate.

Natural Mineral Pigments. There are a number of coloured substances which occur in the earth and these have been used as pigments in various industries for a very long time. These substances, including the siennas, umbers, and ochres are mined in France, Italy, Sicily, Spain, and Cyprus. They consist mainly of oxides of iron and unfortunately they

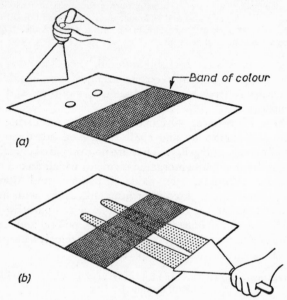

(a)

Band of colour

(b)

Fig. 21.1. Comparing Covering Power

are all dull colours. They suffer a further disadvantage in having low colour strength, which means that a thick film of ink containing these pigments must be applied to give a reasonable depth of shade.

On the other hand they are cheap and have the important advantage of a natural permanence to light. This makes them useful pigments for mixing brownish tints such as the flesh colours necessary in poster printing. Whereas most pigments will fade when drastically reduced with a white pigment (e.g.

100 to 1 with zinc oxide), the earth colours are extremely reliable.

Manufactured Mineral Pigments. The next stage in pigment development was the discovery that naturally occurring mineral substances could be converted into colouring matters by chemical means. A large number of the salts of metals are coloured but relatively few of them have sufficient colour strength or are stable enough to be useful as pigments.

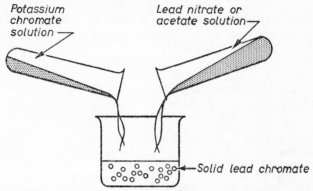

FIG. 21.2. THE FORMATION OF CHROME YELLOW PIGMENT

Among the few that are suitable are some that are of considerable importance to the colour user. The lead chrome group of pigments ranges from a greenish-yellow to a reddish-orange and these pigments are widely used in printing inks. Basically they consist of lead chromate $PbCrO_4$, which is produced when a solution of potassium chromate is added to a solution of lead nitrate or lead acetate.

EXPERIMENT 3. TO PREPARE CHROME YELLOW

Dissolve a small quantity of potassium chromate in some distilled water in a test tube. Make a similar solution of either lead nitrate or lead acetate in a second test tube (Fig. 21.2). Mix the two solutions and filter the yellow precipitate. Wash the pigment in the filter paper with distilled water and if possible dry.

As with many of these inorganic pigments, it is possible to vary their eventual shade by varying the amounts of other chemicals present when the reaction takes place. If the chromate is made alkaline before the lead salt is mixed with it, the pigment which forms is a redder shade of yellow. If a small amount of sodium sulphate is added to the chromate solution, then the shade is a greener yellow.

EXPERIMENT 4. TO PREPARE CHROME ORANGE

Repeat the last experiment making the solution of chromate strongly alkaline with a few drops of concentrated sodium hydroxide solution before mixing with the lead salt. Compare the colour of this pigment with the chrome yellow prepared in the last experiment.

Other important inorganic colours are the iron blues (including bronze blue), ultramarine, and the cadmium pigments. Although the iron blues cover a range of shades they all basically consist of ferric ferrocyanide.

EXPERIMENT 5. TO PREPARE AN IRON BLUE

Make up a solution of potassium ferrocyanide in a test tube and add to a solution of ferrous sulphate. A light blue precipitate of ferrous ferricyanide is formed. The addition of some hydrochloric acid and sodium dichromate will convert this into a deep-blue precipitate of ferric ferricyanide. As with the chrome yellows, the final shade can be varied by changing the acidity of the solution.

The chrome greens are mixtures of the iron blues and chrome yellows, precipitated together by the pigment maker. Generally speaking, these inorganic pigments consist of small hard crystals which are difficult to grind into a vehicle and they tend to give inks with poor working properties on the machines. However, on the credit side they are very fast to light and in many cases to chemicals. Perhaps their greatest advantage is their low cost. They are perfectly adequate for certain types of ink and should continue to find a place in printing. In fact it seems likely that they will regain some of the ground lost to organic pigments (*see* below), as a result of improvements in texture and dispersability being made by the manufacturers. Inorganic pigments are used much more in paint making than in printing inks, since here the demands made on the pigment are quite different.

Organic Pigments. About a hundred years ago the colours so far mentioned were the only ones available for paints and inks. The shade range was not complete and there were no really bright colours. If there is one date worth remembering in the development of colour it must be 1856, for in that year an eighteen-year-old English chemistry student, William Perkin, carried out an experiment which led him unexpectedly to discover the first truly synthetic dyestuff. He patented the method of manufacture and set up a small works near London to exploit the product commercially.

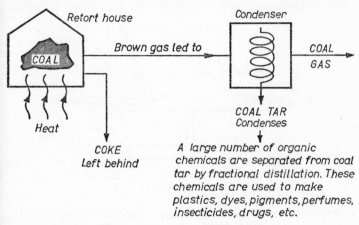

FIG. 21.3. CHEMICALS FROM COAL

Since that time thousands of organic dyes and pigments have been discovered. The raw materials used in the manufacture of organic colouring matters are normally obtained from the distillation of coal. When coal is heated in ovens at a gas works, brown gases are given off and coke is left behind. These gases are led to a condenser where a sticky black tar separates out, and "coal gas" passes on. It is from this black "coal tar" that we obtain a large number of valuable organic chemicals (Fig. 21.3). The colour chemist takes these chemicals and in a series of reactions builds them up into much larger molecules which are coloured dyes and pigments.

These synthetic pigments for printing inks are still being

discovered and developed. One of the last major develop-
ments came in the 1930s when an entirely new range of blue
and green pigments was discovered and later marketed by
I.C.I. under the trade name MONASTRAL. Two of these
remarkably stable colours are now used in making the greenish
blue (cyan) ink for standard three-colour printing.

The use of organic pigments for ink manufacture has been
steadily increasing in recent years. Their great advantages
over the inorganics are their brightness and colour strength.

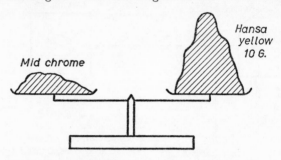

FIG. 21.4. ORGANIC PIGMENTS HAVE LOWER SPECIFIC GRAVITIES
THAN INORGANIC

They have lower specific gravities, e.g. Hansa Yellow 10G
s.g. = 1·1 (cf. Mid Chrome s.g. = 5·8) (Fig. 21.4); and
therefore show less tendency to settle out of an ink in which
they have been dispersed. Their resistance to light, heat and
chemicals varies a great deal. The early synthetic dyes and
pigments were often not very fast to light, but in many cases
their stability has been improved by modifying their physical
form.

EXPERIMENT 6. TO PREPARE A RED ORGANIC PIGMENT

1. Dissolve about 4 c.c. of recently distilled aniline in a solution made
up of 10 c.c. of concentrated hydrochloric acid mixed with 10 c.c. of water.
Cool the solution, preferably by standing it in iced water. Slowly add a
solution of 4 gm of sodium nitrite in 8 c.c. of water, while stirring.

2. Dissolve about 0·5 gm of β-naphthol in a small quantity of concentrated sodium hydroxide solution, and dilute by pouring into about 200 c.c.
of water.

3. Pour into this solution some of the solution prepared in 2. A red pigment forms immediately.

The pigment that is good in every respect does not exist. All pigments, whether they are organic or inorganic have some weakness. For this reason, the ink-maker has to select the pigment for a particular ink with great care. The printer should tell him everything he can about the conditions that the ink is likely to have to stand up to both on the press and later as a print.

Selection for the Process. A particular pigment may not be suitable for all the printing processes. For example, a

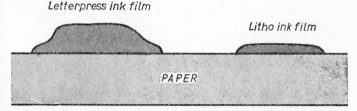

Letterpress ink film

Litho ink film

PAPER

FIG. 21.5. PIGMENTS FOR LITHO INKS MUST HAVE GOOD
COLOUR STRENGTH

lithographic ink must be resistant to water or it is going to "bleed" into the "fountain solution" on the press. Since the film of ink printed by offset lithography may be only two microns thick, the pigments used must have extremely good colour strength (Fig. 21.5). A colour which is very abrasive should not be included in a gravure ink or it will cause excessive wear on the copper printing surface.

Selection for the Job. Where is the ink going to do its work? On a chocolate box or on a tin of baked beans? In a book or on a poster? This knowledge is important to the ink-maker since in all of these tasks, the pigment will have to face a particular set of conditions. Before it can be safely used in an ink, it must be tested. The pigment is used in making a standard ink with a particular vehicle. (*N.B.* A pigment may not behave in the same way in every type of vehicle.) A print is made and when this is properly dry it is ready to be tested.

The tests on ink which we are now going to consider are frequently carried out in the laboratories of the larger printing works, as well as by the ink manufacturers.

Testing for Resistance to Light. The pigment in an ink which is going to be used on a poster or showcard must, above all, have good resistance to the action of light.

EXPERIMENT 7. TESTING FOR LIGHT FASTNESS

Collect together a number of samples of colour printing including some pastel shades. Cover a portion of each print with a strip of sheet metal or some thick white paper and leave outside exposed to a south light for some weeks. At intervals compare the exposed with the unexposed portions and keep a record of your findings. This test can be speeded up in a Fadeometer where the powerful light from a carbon arc can quickly give a guide to the light-fastness of the ink. The results must be carefully interpreted since they do not always agree with those made in natural sunlight.

Testing for Resistance to Water. This can be carried out very simply by immersing part of a test strip in a test tube containing some water. After one hour, remove the print, examine the water for bleed, and compare the shade of the wet areas with that of the dry areas.

Testing for Resistance to Soap. The ink for a soap wrapper or carton should preferably be tested with a sample of the actual soap that is going to be packed.

EXPERIMENT 8. TESTING FOR SOAP RESISTANCE

Prepare a 10 per cent solution of a particular type of soap in water and pour it to cool in a shallow dish or tray. When a gel has formed, lay a number of small portions of various prints on the surface of the soap with their printed sides down. After thirty minutes, remove the prints and closely examine the surface of the soap for traces of colour which have transferred from the print.

Testing for Resistance to Acids and Alkalis. Inks which can resist these chemicals are often required in packaging. Soaps may be weakly or strongly alkaline, and several foodstuffs are faintly acid. Litho inks must have reasonable acid resistance since "fountain solutions" are generally slightly acidic.

EXPERIMENT 9. TESTING FOR ACID AND ALKALI RESISTANCE

Immerse portions of test strips in two test tubes, one containing 8 per cent sodium hydroxide solution and the other 20 per cent hydrochloric acid solution. After one hour, remove the strips, examine the solutions for bleed and compare the shades with those of the untreated areas.

To carry out the tests covering the most common causes of chemical fading PATRA recommend the following solutions: 20 per cent hydrochloric acid, 30 per cent acetic acid, 8 per cent sodium hydroxide, 10 per cent sodium carbonate, 14 per cent sodium sulphite, 10 per cent sodium metabisulphite.

Testing for the Presence of Lead. Lead compounds are poisonous and so inks for food packages should preferably be completely free from lead. Some chocolate manufacturers insist on this and carry out their own tests on the printed cartons. Lead could be present in the form of a chrome yellow pigment or as lead driers. These precautions are sensible, but it has been calculated that a large number of cartons would have to be eaten before there were any serious effects!

EXPERIMENT 10. TESTING FOR THE PRESENCE OF LEAD

Place a small portion of an ink in the bottom of a crucible and heat it over a Bunsen in a fume cupboard. When the ink ceases to glow red, remove the burner. Whilst the ash is still warm, add about 5 c.c. of a 10 per cent solution of acetic acid. Mix thoroughly with a clean glass rod and then filter into a clean test tube. To this clear solution add a few drops of potassium chromate solution. A yellow precipitate indicates the presence of lead. If the result is negative, repeat the experiment using an ink which you know contains a lead chrome pigment.

Testing for Resistance to Solvents. Inks for labels that are later going to be lacquered or spirit varnished must resist the particular solvent that is going to be used. The solvent for many label varnishes is industrial methylated spirits.

EXPERIMENT 11. TESTING FOR SOLVENT RESISTANCE

Method. Immerse a portion of a test strip in a test tube containing some methylated spirits. After half an hour examine the solvent for bleed and the print for change of shade.

These are just a few of the more important tests which are made on printing inks in order to show that the pigments chosen will do their job satisfactorily. Other properties include resistance to heat (tin box printing), resistance to molten wax (waxed cartons), resistance to fats (butter, margarine, and cooking-fat packs) and complete freedom from odour. More than one test is in use for most of these properties.

THINGS TO LEARN

1. Pigments are insoluble coloured substances.
2. To be suitable for a printing ink a pigment must have—

    (*a*) good stability to light and chemicals;
    (*b*) good colour strength;
    (*c*) fine particle size;
    (*d*) the ability to be dispersed in normal vehicles.

3. Pigments for printing inks fall into the following groups—

    (*a*) carbon black, obtained by burning natural gas in a limited supply of air;
    (*b*) natural inorganic pigments, e.g. iron oxide pigments;
    (*c*) manufactured inorganic pigments, e.g. alumina, titanium dioxide, chrome yellow;
    (*d*) synthetic organic pigments (the largest group), e.g. "Monastral" blue.

4. Printing ink pigments must be suitable for—

    (*a*) the printing process (letterpress, litho, gravure, etc.);
    (*b*) the job, which may demand resistance to light, acids, alkalis, solvents, fats, heat, etc.

OTHER BOOKS TO READ

H. J. WOLFE, *Printing and Litho Inks* (McNair-Dorland Co.)

CARLTON ELLIS, *Printing Inks* (Reinhold Publishing Corp.)

E. A. APPS, *Printing Ink Technology* (L. Hill)

P. J. HARTSUCH, *The Chemistry of Lithography* (Lithographic Technical Foundation)

R. F. BOWLES (ED.), *Printing Ink Manual* (Heffer)

EXERCISES

1. Write brief notes on: (a) carbon black; (b) inorganic pigments; and (c) organic pigments.

2. Compare the properties of inorganic and organic pigments in relation to their use in printing inks.

3. Describe tests which you could carry out to check the resistance of a dry print or a coloured binding material to acids, alkalis, and light.

4. Describe a method of testing for the presence of lead in a printing ink. Explain why this test should ever be necessary and which of the materials in the ink are likely to contain lead.

5. A firm is producing posters, soapwrappers, chocolate cartons, and playing cards. What end-product testing would it be sensible to introduce for each of these products. Describe how three of the tests you mention are carried out.

CHAPTER 22

MAKING THINGS STICK

In the bindery and warehouse, in carton and box making, printers have to find ways and means of making a permanent attachment between two different materials. Any liquid which wets both materials will cause them to stick together for a time, but to form a permanent joint we have to use the substances known as *adhesives*. Choosing the adhesive most suitable for the particular job in hand demands some knowledge of why materials stick together.

ADHESION

The force holding two surfaces together is called the force of adhesion. It may arise from either or both of two quite separate and distinct effects. In one case the adhesive penetrates into holes in the two surfaces to be stuck together like a flat piece of Plasticine pressed between two bits of wire gauze (Fig. 22.1 (*a*)). This type of mechanical adhesion depends on the strength of the key and can be used satisfactorily only when the surfaces involved allow penetration by the adhesive. In the other case adhesion is due to the forces of attraction between the molecules of the adhesive and the molecules of the surface to which it is applied—a force somewhat similar to that responsible for surface tension (Fig. 22.1 (*b*)).

When two glass plates are wetted and placed together it is very difficult to pull them apart, and a fair amount of force is needed even to slide one over the other. This is partly because the water molecules and the glass molecules attract each other strongly. As the water evaporates the force of adhesion disappears. The printer's problem is to maintain the force of attraction after the adhesive has dried. Substances used as adhesives are usually molecules made up of long chains of atoms arranged in such a way that at each end of the chain is a group which has a strong attraction for either one or the other of the two materials to be stuck together.

The first requirement of any adhesive is that it should wet the *adherend*, as the material to which it is applied is called. If it does not do so then no bond of either kind can be formed. In the case of mechanical adhesion there must be some penetration of the adhesive into the adherend to give the necessary key.

In most printing applications it is necessary that the dried film of adhesive should be flexible to ensure that it does not

(a)

(b)

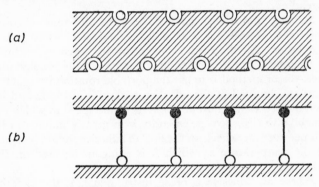

FIG. 22.1. FORMS OF ADHESION

crack when the paper, board, or cloth to which it is attached is bent. Air bubbles and points of internal stress due to uneven drying should also be avoided as the strength of an adhesive layer is the strength of its weakest point. Most bookbinders will have seen the crazing of glue due to cracks spreading from points of internal stress.

Printers also need to ensure that the pH of an adhesive will not affect the dyes or pigments used in colouring paper, cloth, or other binding material. There are plenty of examples of adhesives causing covers to discolour because an acid adhesive was used with a non-acid-resistant cover or an alkaline adhesive with a material not alkali-resistant.

Flow of Adhesives. Because paper and board are absorbent materials the viscosity of adhesives to be used with them is of even greater importance than when the adherend is non-absorbent. With any material the adhesive must flow freely enough to allow easy and even spread over the required area. Where the adherend is absorbent, however, too low a viscosity may lead to so much adhesive soaking into the surface that insufficient is left to give adequate bonding to the other adherend. On the other hand, where the viscosity is too high penetration into the material may be insufficient to produce effective keying in addition to the difficulties arising from poor spreading.

Striking the right balance between different viscosity requirements calls for a reliable method of measuring flow properties. All the methods of measuring viscosity outlined in Chapter 8 can be applied to adhesives but the simplest and most direct method is to use the portable rotation viscometer. This can be used in the adhesive tank of a machine and set to the speed range most appropriate to the speed at which the machine works. Because viscosity is so greatly influenced by temperature any check on the flow of adhesive should be made at the temperature at which it is going to be used on the machine.

Where an adhesive is being distributed hot, the viscosity may be far below the figure at which it will penetrate too rapidly into the adherend. But where it cools rapidly on contact with the surface the increase in viscosity due to this cooling may be enough to prevent trouble arising. It is possible therefore to adjust the working temperature so as to get the best of both effects—easy running on the machine without excess penetration.

It should be remembered that the flow of an adhesive is affected by the amount of solid material it contains as well as by the temperature. If it is allowed to lose water or solvent in the tank it will get more and more viscous as the run goes on and what started as an adhesive with the right flow properties may begin to cause trouble through faulty distribution or failure to penetrate sufficiently.

Viscosity–temperature curves of adhesives are often good guides to their suitability for in-line operations. The surface of the adhesive must retain enough fluidity to form an effective joint when the second adherend is pressed on, yet setting should have advanced far enough for the work to proceed to the next operation. By then it should not be necessary to wait long before the joint has reached sufficient strength for further handling. For hot glues viscosity–temperature curves will give this information, while for cold glues a graph showing the increase of viscosity with solid content will be more suitable.

Animal, Vegetable, and Mineral. Adhesives used in printing and bookbinding come from a wide variety of sources, including animal, vegetable, and mineral, as well as the modern synthetics. These last have become increasingly popular of recent years. Vegetable and animal adhesives, like all natural products of this kind, tend to vary in properties from batch to batch and are less reliable than the more predictable synthetics. Other advantages of synthetic adhesives are that most of them work cold, have permanent flexibility, and are not affected by atmospheric changes, nor attacked by bacteria, moulds, and insects.

Glues are made by heating animal bones, skin, and hides with water to produce an impure form of gelatin. To give flexibility to the dried film, sugars, glycerin, and glycol are added. These help the film to take up moisture from the atmosphere and so prevent it from drying out completely to the original brittle form.

Pastes and natural cold glues are usually based on starch obtained from potatoes, grain, tapioca, and similar starchy vegetables. In the original starch form they are rather slow in drying, but the starch can be processed to give the much faster dextrin, which is a product half way between starch and sugar. Other vegetable adhesives are the gums, such as gum arabic and gum tragacanth, which are the exudations of various trees, although it should be noted that the well-known crystal gum is a purified form of dextrin.

All these natural adhesives suffer from the disadvantage that they can become breeding grounds for bacteria especially in warm and humid conditions. They also allow the tiny spores of moulds and fungi, small enough to get through most air filters, to develop into the large colonies which are so common as patches of mould on bindings. The starch-based adhesives are natural food for a range of insects, as well as mice, which eat their way through the covers of books to get at the tasty starch or dextrin in the adhesive layer. Alum or carbolic acid can be added in small quantities to act as antiseptics and prevent the bacteria developing. There is also a wide range of fungicides, including copper sulphate, which may be used to limit the growth of moulds. A good deal of work is still being done at PATRA to find the best additives for discouraging bacteria, moulds, and insects from attacking books and packages.

Latex adhesives may be based on the sap of the rubber tree or on the polymers which go to make up synthetic rubber. Used alone or in combination with other adhesives they give a very flexible joint which is especially suitable for bonding paper with other materials.

The most common of the synthetic adhesives in use in book-binding is polyvinyl acetate, usually as an emulsion and sometimes combined with a latex. Many other resins are used, especially for heat-fix and pressure adhesives. Resins based on formaldehyde are employed for jobs where the strength of the paper needs to be maintained while it is still wet. Synthetic adhesives are often "tailor-made" for a particular use and therefore a product which gives good results in one case will not necessarily be the right adhesive for a different application. It is far from safe to mix adhesives unless it is known that they are of similar composition.

THINGS TO LEARN

1. Adhesion may be obtained by means of mechanical or molecular forces, the former being used only with absorbent materials.

2. The viscosity of an adhesive is the property which is decisive in affecting its working qualities.

3. Natural adhesives are liable to attack by bacteria, moulds, and insects. Synthetic adhesives are not.

OTHER BOOKS TO READ

J. Hurd, *Adhesives Guide* (British Scientific Instrument Research Assn.)

EXERCISES

1. What are the two main types of force involved in adhesion? Explain why some degree of penetration of the adherend is necessary with one of these types.

2. Glues tend to be acidic and pastes alkaline. If this chemical activity is at all excessive it may cause difficulties with other bookbinding materials. (a) Describe these difficulties and relate each to the general properties of acids and alkalis. (b) Outline and briefly explain a method of measuring the acidity or alkalinity of adhesives. (PEB/1960/Fin.)

3. A glue which works satisfactorily on a cold morning fails to give adequate adhesion as the temperature of the bindery rises later in the day. Give your opinion of the most likely cause of the trouble.

4. What types of adhesive are liable to be attacked by moulds and insects? Name two substances which may be used to prevent this type of attack.

5. List the advantages of synthetic adhesives over those obtained from natural materials. Give two substances employed as synthetic adhesives in bookbinding.

6. Some papers have been found to be more strongly held by perfect binding than by sewn binding. What would be the main characteristics of these papers?

CHAPTER 23

BINDING MATERIALS

Most of the properties of paper and board of importance in the bindery are already dealt with in previous chapters. Resistance to tear is an obvious need in the case of papers to be used with sewn binding and a fair degree of absorbency is essential where so-called perfect binding is to be used. There are many other materials used in binding, however, including the all-important series of leathers.

Decay of Leather. Following a marked increase in the decay of leather bindings in the later years of the nineteenth century a full-scale investigation of the causes was undertaken. This led to the discovery that all leathers build up a content of sulphuric acid during their lifetime owing to the presence of sulphur dioxide in the atmosphere. Sulphur dioxide is contained in quite large quantities in the fumes from solid fuels and from gas burners. Absorbed by the leather it is transformed into sulphuric acid by the catalytic action of minute quantities of various metals contained in the tanned skins. Although the acid content increased in all leathers, it attacked the fibre structure only in those cases where washing or the method of tanning had removed from the skins protective agents which were soluble in water. This internal protection can be restored to the leather by treating it with a weak solution of potassium lactate, the recommended strength being 7 per cent. Many of the bookbinding leathers now available have been treated in this way and will stand the test of time.

HURRYING UP NATURE

If we want to know whether or not a leather is likely to decay we cannot wait twenty or thirty years for it to happen in the natural course of events. We must hurry up nature by some form of accelerated ageing test. For this purpose the forerunner of PATRA, the Printing Industry Research Association, devised what is known as the PIRA test. This is the addition to the leather of sulphuric acid followed by the further addition of an oxidizing agent so that in a few days the leather experiences the treatment it would suffer during twenty years or more of exposure to the atmosphere of an industrial town.

The method of test is as follows. A piece of leather between two and three inches square is weighed in its air-dry condition and laid on a glass plate with the flesh side uppermost. It is wetted evenly with a normal solution of sulphuric acid (49 gm concentrated sulphuric acid per litre), 1 c.c. of the solution being added per gramme of leather. After the leather has dried again in the air, hydrogen peroxide at 10 volumes strength is added, in this case the dose being 0·6 gm per gramme of leather. Five further treatments with the same amount of hydrogen peroxide are made at 24-hr. intervals with the leather exposed to the atmosphere for the whole time. At the end of seven days the leather is compared with the original untreated material. If the leather subjected to the test has lost its suppleness, cracks on bending or blackens on the edges it is not durable and will be liable to rot with prolonged use. Leathers guaranteed to withstand this test can be bought from most manufacturers.

EXPERIMENT 1. TO TEST THE PROTECTION GIVEN TO LEATHER BY POTASSIUM LACTATE

Apparatus. Large glass plate; 7 per cent solution of potassium lactate; normal sulphuric acid; 10 volume hydrogen peroxide.

From a number of samples of leather (not guaranteed against the PIRA test) cut three similar test pieces each about 2½ in. square. Place one sample of each in a row at the top of the glass plate. Note the weight in grammes of each of the other samples of the respective leathers and soak one of each in the potassium lactate solution. When these have dried in the air, place them on the plate underneath the corresponding control pieces, and make up a third row from the remaining pieces. Now carry out the PIRA test on the lower two rows, comparing all three rows at the end of seven days. It will be found that the leather treated with potassium lactate will have withstood the test while the third row will be badly affected.

Chemical Fading. When the experiment outlined above is carried out, it may be found that some of the leathers change colour even though they are not affected in any other way.

This is due to the dyes used being changed in colour by the acid in the same way as dyes and pigments used in paper and printing ink may be subject to chemical fading. Coloured leather, rexine, cloth, paper, board, etc., may be tested for their liability to fade in a variety of conditions in the same way and with the same six solutions as are set out in Chapter 21. They may also be tested for their light fastness as described in the same chapter.

In binding and warehouse work much of the chemical fading encountered is due to chemical reaction between the adhesive used and the colouring matter in the cover material. A chemical fading test will show within an hour whether it is safe to use an acid or alkaline adhesive with any particular material.

Tarnishing. When bindings are blocked with metallic foil one of the aspects with which the binder is concerned will be their liability to tarnishing. In the case of real gold foil tarnishing will not take place, although with some types of plastic that have been used in binding even gold foil has been damaged by the action of plasticizers, the high boiling point solvents used to give flexibility to the material.

Silver foil, on the other hand, may be tarnished by the action of sulphuretted hydrogen in the atmosphere and even more rapidly by reducible sulphur in the material to which it is attached. The same is true of brass or other foil containing copper, both copper and silver sulphide being black. The presence of reducible sulphur may be detected by the same test as is applied to paper. This test is described in Chapter 19.

Tarnishing of aluminium foil arises in other ways, but aluminium can be given a high degree of protection by the process of anodizing which forms a thin layer of aluminium oxide on the surface. This layer may be brightly coloured by the addition of dyestuffs during anodizing, and many coloured foils prepared in this way retain their brightness almost indefinitely.

THINGS TO LEARN

1. Decay of leather is due to the building up of sulphuric

acid in the leather by the oxidation of sulphur dioxide absorbed from the atmosphere.

2. Decay may be prevented by treating the leather with a 7 per cent solution of potassium lactate.

3. Tarnishing of silver- and copper-based foils is due to the formation of black sulphides under the action of sulphuretted hydrogen.

OTHER BOOKS TO READ

H. J. PLENDERLEITH, *The Preservation of Leather Bookbindings* (British Museum)

EXERCISES

1. Outline the process by which a bookbinding leather decays. What substance can be added to the leather to prevent this decay?

2. Describe how you would test a number of samples of leather for their durability. What specification would you include with an order for book-binding leather if you wished to ensure that it would not be liable to decay rapidly?

3. A material to be blocked with imitation gold foil is believed to be liable to cause tarnishing of the foil. How would you check whether or not this was the case and are there any steps you can take to minimize the trouble?

4. A green drawn-on cover has turned yellow down the spine. What is the most likely cause and how do you think it could have been avoided?

APPENDIX

ADDITIONAL EXPERIMENTAL WORK

IN the foregoing text there are set out over 40 experiments which can be carried out with a minimum of equipment and many other simple experiments are indicated in the general run of the text. Most printing students benefit from the opportunity for learning offered by a more complete course of practical work, especially when the experiments are carried out on materials in use in the craft workshops and the tests of materials are part of the normal routine of the workshop. Listed here are a number of additional experiments which it would be useful to include. The methods of carrying them out will be found in the books recommended for further reading.

GROUP 1 (BASIC SCIENCE)

Mixtures and compounds—Materials A and B in the experiment given in Chapter 3 are sulphur and salt (A) and sulphur and iron filings (B). Many other mixtures including mixtures of pigments can be used.

Crookes tube showing electron stream.

Density by measuring and weighing.

Further specific gravity determinations.

Making a test-tube hydrometer.

Use of hydrometer with solutions of increasing concentration.

Making a thermometer.

Making a thermostat with a bimetallic strip.

Measuring dew point.

Constructing simple machines and pulley systems of given mechanical advantage.

Effect of lubrication on efficiency of a simple machine.

Measuring coefficient of friction.

Making a falling sphere viscometer in a test tube.

Further experiments with each type of chemical reaction.

Gain and loss in weight during oxidation of metals and reduction of oxides.
Elementary titrations.
Inverse square law by photometry.
Position of images in inclined mirrors.
Position of images in concave mirrors.
Use of the pin-hole camera.
Construction of a simple camera.
Refractive index by real and apparent depth of glass block.
Measurement of critical angle.
Focal length of lens combinations.
Change of electrical resistance with temperature.
Measurement of resistance by Wheatstone bridge.
Determination of electrochemical equivalent of copper.

GROUP 2 (APPLIED SCIENCE)

Measurement of machine parts, type height, caliper of paper, board, platemaking metals.
Recording of relative humidity of workshop and laboratory.
Determining moisture content of paper.
Chemical fading tests on ink films and coloured materials.
Tests for solvent resistance, soap resistance, etc.
Rub resistance of ink films and binding materials.
Effect of pH on ink drying time (Print Drying Time Tester).
Effect of driers on drying time.
Construction of model of optical system for filmsetting.
Influence of light intensity and colour on exposure time.
Colour matching with PATRA water colours and inks.
Measurement of colour by spectrophotometer.
Making letterpress and litho inks on a 3-roll mill.
Making gravure inks on a ball mill.
Identifying furnish of paper with microscope.
Microscopic examination of printing surfaces, paper surfaces, printing defects, alloy structure, fungus, folds, and creases.
Effect of impurities in type alloys.
Testing paper for machine direction, dimensional stability, surface oil absorption, opacity, gloss, pick, micro-contours. K & N ink test.

Use of stack thermometer, sword hygrometer and PATRA PET in workshops.

pH measurement of paper extracts, fountain solutions, and adhesives.

Effect of concentration on etching reactions.

Effect on dichromated colloids of pH, amount of dichromate, temperature.

Effect of temperature on speed of development.

ANSWERS TO EXERCISES

CHAPTER 2 (p. 22)

1. (a) 4 yd 6 in.; (b) 3·56 cm; (c) 13 kg 620 gm. 2. 0·426 sq. m.
4. (a) 1·16; (b) 3·92; (c) 3·09.

CHAPTER 3 (p. 41)

4. Al:Ag 4:1.

CHAPTER 4 (p. 50)

4. 88·09 c.c. and 370·37 c.c. 5. 16 cm. 6. 80 c.c. 7. 0·34 c.c.

CHAPTER 5 (p. 66)

2. 377°C. 4. 2,373·6 cal.

CHAPTER 6 (p. 81)

2. 5 lb wt. 5. 16,720 ft lb wt., and 0·25 h.p. 6. 64·3 per cent. 7. 5 in.

CHAPTER 7 (p. 89)

1. 10·4 lb per sq. in. 2. 6,000 lb wt. 3. 20 lb per sq. in. 4. 288.

CHAPTER 9 (p. 112)

7. 222·5 gm. 9. 1,562·5 gm.

CHAPTER 10 (p. 124)

1. 30 gm. 2. 21 oz. 4. (a) 19·75 per cent; (b) 39·75 per cent. 5. (b)
10·55 lb. 6. 2,500 lb.

CHAPTER 12 (p. 167)

1. 428,600,000,000,000 waves per second. 2. (b) $\frac{16}{49}$. 4. (a) $12\frac{1}{2}$ min.
12. (a) $v = 36$ in. $u = 36$ in.; (b) $v = 31\frac{1}{2}$ in. $u = 42$ in.; (c) $v = 22\frac{1}{2}$ in.
$u = 90$ in. 13. (c) $M = 2$.

CHAPTER 18 (p. 248)

2. No, 10 amp is current needed. 3. App. 6d. 8. 3,125 watts; 1·25
amp; 6·25 amp; 5·0 amp.

INDEX